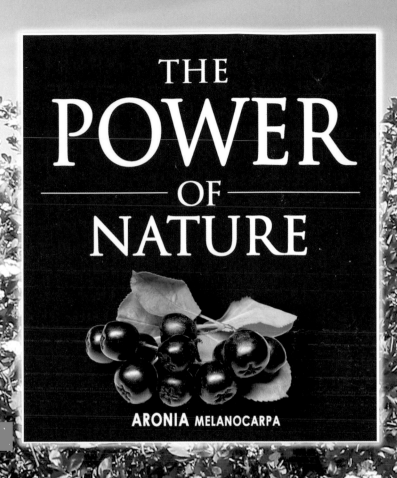

THE
POWER
OF
NATURE

ARONIA MELANOCARPA

D1092143

PROFESSOR IWONA WAWER

Medical Disclaimer.
The information in this book is for educational purposes only and the
opinions expressed are those of the author. Persons with medical problems
should consult a physician or other healthcare professional. The information
in this book is not intended to diagnose or self-medicate any disease.
It is not to be taken as medical advice or as an attempt to sell a
particular product.

This book is dedicated to health care professionals and the consumers
willing to learn about Aronia berries.

Production
Silvio Mattacchione and Co.
1251 Scugog Line 8, R.R. #1
Port Perry, ON, Canada L9L 1B2
Telephone: 905-985-3555
Fax: 416-987-9444

silvio@silvio-co.com
www.silvio-co.com

Production by A-R Bookbuilders
Printed in Singapore

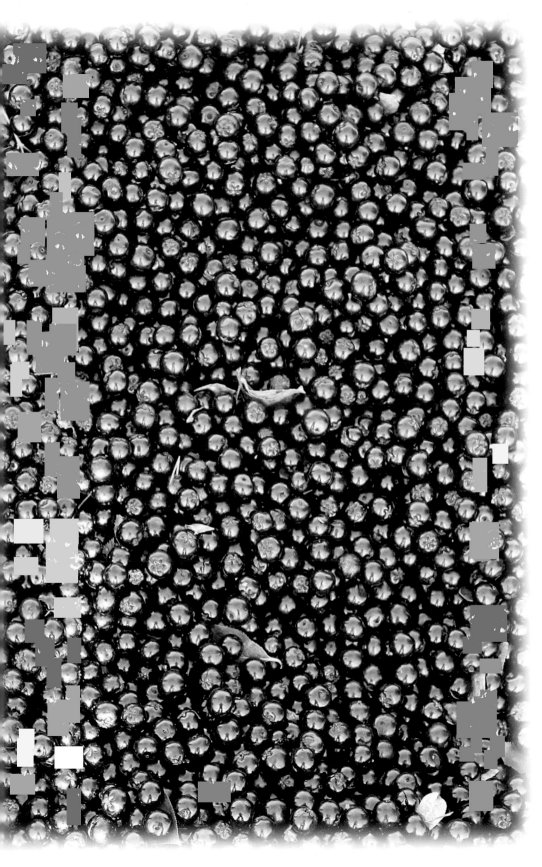

TABLE OF CONTENTS

PUBLISHER'S INTRODUCTION

For over 20 years, I have been an advocate of nutrition based health and wellness.

I became engrained in the cause in the mid 1990's after discovering the amazing health benefits of the Aronia berry. I wanted to learn everything I could about this dark purple super-fruit. Planting, cultivating and maintaining Aronia berry bushes for inclusion into my personal daily diet were the first steps in a long journey.

As I began to share my findings and the berries from my plants with friends, family and neighbors they began telling me how great the Aronia berry was and the positive effects it was having on their health and wellness. I quickly came to believe that the Aronia berry was truly, one of nature's healers and protectors, and my passion for this super-berry soon became very personal.

My brother Johnny was diagnosed with liver failure. His health rapidly deteriorated and his weight dropped dramatically. We incorporated Aronia berries into his daily diet, and I saw my brother's weight increase and his overall health improve. He slowly began to feel better and even returned to work for many years. While my brother ultimately lost his battle in 2009, I know that the health benefits of the Aronia berry gave Johnny additional, quality time that he was able to spend with our family.

After this personal experience with Aronia and how it dramatically changed the lives of my family and friends, I made it my life's mission to share information about this little known but powerful berry with everyone who would listen. I thought I had read everything available on Aronia and then one day, while researching on-line, I found it….the Aronia handbook. There it was in front of me, like a beacon, a book dedicated solely to Aronia called, "The Power of Nature - Aronia Melanocarpa – Nature Combined with Health" by Professor Iwona Wawer of Poland.

Dr. Wawer, as I soon discovered, is exceedingly accomplished; The Head of the Department of Physical Chemistry, Faculty of Pharmacy, Medical University of Warsaw, The Head of The Scientific Committee of the Polish Council for Supplements & Nutritional Foods. A scientist and fellow champion of Aronia, a professional dedicated to making the Aronia berry known throughout the world. I ordered the book and when I received it, I ripped it out of the envelope, and read it from cover-to-cover. I have to say that few findings in the book really surprised me. What I had been seeing for years in the lives of so many was now being supported by the science and findings of Dr. Wawer.

As time went on I was lucky enough to meet with Dr. Wawer and together we recommitted to a mutual mission — to share information about Aronia to help those in need, and with anyone who wants to feel better, and enhance their general health.

I feel honored to have my comments included in the North American edition of this incredible book. Dr. Wawer does an outstanding job explaining the power of Aronia Melanocarpa and how this dark-purple berry contains properties that are essential for health and wellness.

I urge you to read this book, discover the power of Aronia and experience personally "The Power of Nature".

Kenny Sailors
Aronia Pioneer & Enthusiast
Owner of Mae's Health and Wellness
Superberries.com

FOREWORD
BY DR. DINUCCI

This book should be in every doctor's library and on everyone's must read list.

As a physician, I have not seen anything like the Aronia berry or its potential in healing the human body. I have countless examples of patients with chronic disease or daily pain or wounds that won't heal that have experienced a remarkable change in their conditions after consuming this powerful berry.

We are fortunate to have this great work from Dr. Wawer as she gives a very concise and detailed view of the Aronia berry, from the botanical sense of how it is grown, to the biochemical pathways of how the different components of the berry interact in our bodies, stimulate healing and promote anti-aging. Importantly, she doesn't just state her opinion on the value of the Aronia berry, she presents new scientific evidence on the healing potential for each natural and chemical component of this "superberry".

Many countries and societies suffer from a cultural disease of fast-food and frozen dinners and choose convenience over nutrition. In a world where more of our food is processed and refined, nutrients are scarce.

With this book we have a scientific look at a natural berry that offers the possibility of countering the negative diet choices we make every day. I believe that if every physician utilized the knowledge presented by Dr. Wawer, the cultural disease we suffer from as a country would be seriously challenged.

Without the help of Ken Sailors, Scott Carlson and Dr. Wawer another generation may have passed before we discovered the hidden secrets that lie within the amazing Aronia berry. Thank you to everyone who has helped to bring this book to the English speaking world. We can now continue to realize the potential that this berry has held for so many years.

Dr. Kent DiNucci

Fellow of the American College of Foot and Ankle Surgeons

PREFACE

Poland constitutes a bridge between the East and the West of Europe and now, has a chance to introduce many traditional foods into the European Union market. Some of the best-known Polish specialities are borsch (a beetroot soup), dumplings (a Russian recipe), bigos (a cabbage stew) or smoked sheep's cheese. However, the biggest hit that could revolutionize European menus and eating habits may be… the Black Chokeberry (Aronia). Fortunately, Polish agriculture may supply pure, ecological products: fruit, vegetables and herbs. Fresh, frozen or processed fruit and vegetables, as well as preparations made of them, can improve the health of the aging European population, and support the fight against degenerative diseases.

Why am I so optimistic and why do I consider small, black berries as a hope for the well-being of western society?

The answer lies in the scientific findings confirming the unique chemical composition of these berries. First, they were treated only as a source of natural dye, but in the course of detection and isolation of further compounds the enthusiasm

increased. These compounds have strong antioxidant, radical scavenging properties, and most of them are known for their biological activity.

Aronia berries processed as juice, jam, syrup or powdered extract may be considered functional foods which means that they are beneficial for human health. The intake of Aronia foods and antho-cyanin-rich food supplements helps to protect the body against atherosclerosis, hypertension, heart attack and stroke, neurodegenerative diseases, and slows down the aging process.

Wine is a well-known beverage and the procedure for its production is older than Christianity. Wine is mentioned several times in the Bible (for example, a widely known event involving the lack of wine during a wedding in Galilee). In the early 1990's, red wine became an exploding field of scientific interest. The discovery that the intake of saturated fat among the French is similar to that of other developed countries while the mortality rate connected with the death from coronary disease in France is only one third of the average, has become known as the

"**French paradox**" (section 8.3). One distinctive feature was the regular consumption of red wine with meals. Numerous studies confirmed that moderate wine consumption reduces the risk for cardiovascular diseases. This cardioprotective effect has been attributed to the polyphenolic compounds, mainly **anthocyanins** that are responsible for the beautiful, dark red color of wine.

China is the homeland of tea, another plant important for human health. The consumption of tea was initiated here more than five thousand years ago, and it has always been associated with life style and rituals. Tea contains a large amount of biologically active polyphenols, called **catechins**. Recent scientific evidence about the health benefits of tea suggests that these polyphenols possess a high antioxidant power, which can protect cells against oxidative damage.

Aronia combines health beneficial properties of red wine and green tea – the berries contain both types of polyphenols: anthocyanins and catechins.

Two great civilizations, the Mediterranean, cultivating grapes, admiring wine and the Far-Eastern one cultivating tea trees, admiring green tea are complemented by a third, the North-European one – cultivating and appreciating berries, such as: blueberries, black currant, strawberry, elderberry and Aronia.

In northern countries neither grapes or tea can be cultivated and the cold climate favors berries. People feel free to walk and pick berries in the woods or fields. The use of wild fruit and berries has a long tradition in cooking and for therapeutical purposes. Recently, scientists showed that berries are rich in phenolic compounds, essential nutritional components and are precious for human health. The high consumption of berries can significantly reduce the incidence of cardiovascular disease, cancers and other degenerative diseases caused by oxidative stress.

Opponents say that in the 21st century we do not need to pick berries in the woods. Importing

11

goods, even from very distant countries is not a problem. Vineyards are spread over southern Europe and all over the world. High quality wine from France, Italy, Chile, South Africa or USA is not expensive. Citizens of North-European countries may benefit from drinking red wine to the same extent as the French do. However, caution is required when formulating recommendations for daily consumption of alcohol.

Fast and beautiful ships, called the clippers, transported tea to Europe, sailing around the Cape of Good Hope some 200 years ago. Today, there are many kinds of tea, collected in the gardens of India, China and Indonesia. Fresh leaves are processed for the production of green, oolong or black teas. Moving from the traditional beverage, tea is now becoming popular as a healthy drink. Nevertheless, Europeans and Americans did not get the feeling for green tea, even though flavoured and not all people tolerate caffeine well.

Everybody can eat fruit, berries and drink fruit juices. Such juice is a refreshing beverage because it can be consumed by school children and seniors, and can be served at any meal. Without free access to fruit or juice, or in the case when higher doses of antioxidants are required, a capsule containing fruit extract is a rational alternative.

Aronia is a rich source of antioxidants, promising for their cardiovascular protective effects. Increased consumption of Aronia may lower the risk of heart disease; it creates a chance for a "Polish antioxidant paradox".

The experiments performed in vitro and *in vivo* demonstrated that polyphenolic compounds, such as anthocyanins and catechins, could offer significant antiatherogenic protection by inhibiting the oxidation of low-density lipoproteins. Antioxidants, like those found in Aronia can play an important role in the prevention of cancers, of the immune system decline, or of the brain dysfunction (Alzheimer and Parkinson diseases, senile dementia). They may alleviate arthritis and allergies, and can improve other diseases that involve an inflammation component. The antioxidants are, to some extent, responsible for keeping us young, healthy and smart.

To illustrate the remarkable health potential of berries, Dr. Ronald L. Prior, director of USDA studies at Tufts, explains that just a half-cup of blueberries can provide as much antioxidant power as 5 servings of other nutritious fruits and vegetables. While research is ongoing, the results so far have been very promising. "In the meantime," says Prior, "I'm eating blueberries every day."

Anthocyanin, the pigment that makes a blueberry blue, is thought to be the major contributor to the high antioxidant activity levels discovered in chokeberries.

Chokeberries are now gaining recognition as nature's antioxidant powerhouse. Chokeberries rank number one among dozens of fruits, vegetables and juices tested for the antioxidant capacity.

While investigating Aronia's antioxidant power and learning more about its unique biochemistry, my health-conscious colleagues from the Medical University and the Life Sciences University of Warsaw started to drink Aronia juice every day. Some even freeze Aronia berries for winter. Practical and effective is to take the extract of Aronia in capsules, as a dietary supplement. However, we do not want to keep these discoveries secret, we want to share our knowledge with others. That is the aim of this book.

ARONIA:
WILD IN AMERICA,
CULTIVATED IN EUROPE

Aronia or black chokeberry belongs to the Rosaceases family; it is a shrub, native to the north-eastern and north-central United States and adjacent parts of Canada. In its homeland, which is spread from the Great Lakes down to Florida, three kinds of Aronia species can be found:

- **Aronia melanocarpa**, with black fruits

- **Aronia arbutifolia** with red fruits, similar to rowan berries

- **Aronia prunifolia**

At the beginning of the 20th century Aronia came to Europe, first to Russia and Scandinavia and later to Poland and Austria. In the 1930's it became a subject of interest for Ivan Mitchurin, a famous Russian botanist. He was looking for fruits with high nutritional value, easy to cultivate, resistant to cold climate, and could survive heavy frost. Aronia met his expectations, and the Russian genotype was named Aronia mitschurinii. It is cultivated on an industrial scale near Moscow and St. Petersburg, as well as in the Altai Mountains (Aronia mandschurica). The Russian popular name for Aronia can be translated as "black rowanberry", while the Germans call it "schwarze Apfelbeere" – the dark berry really resembles a small apple. However, in western European countries Aronia remained almost unknown, and even specialists frequently used incorrect botanical names, such as Sorbus melanocarpa, Pyrus melanocarpa or Aronia nigra.

Aronia is a shrub 2-2.5 m high, but in fertile soils may grow up to 3m.

The shrubs grow fast and the plantation can be cultivated even for 15-20 years. The most productive are twigs between 2 to 6 years old; older ones are removed because they are not elastic enough for harvesting machinery.

Aronia likes the sun and buoyant air circulation. It is not finicky about soil, but sandy soils are less suitable because they dry out too fast. As mentioned above, it is resistant to low temperatures in winter. It is well known that among all the studied factors (spring frosts, precipitation and a number of days with rain, temperature at noon) spring frosts caused the highest yield loses in European orchards.

Blossoming, which is an important part of the chokeberry production cycle, occurs in the middle of May, later than all other fruit trees in Poland. For this reason Aronia is usually not touched by the spring frosts.

In small home gardens, Aronia shrubs, blossoming with white flowers, are very decorative; likewise in autumn, when the leaves turn to the orange-red color.

They are often so loaded with blossoms, that from a distance, they look like white clouds dotting the land-scape. It is a great

time to visit Poland!

Aronia fruits become dark-blue and ripe after 3 months and the crops are collected in August or at the beginning of September. One bunch includes up to 15 berries of 1-1.5 g each. Anywhere from 10 to over 15 kg may be harvested from a single bush.

The first Aronia plants were brought to Poland from Russia (previously Soviet Union). Aronia can be propagated by seeds or cuttings and both ways have been successfully used in Poland. The first nursery which propagated Aronia by cuttings, and the first Polish industrial plantation, were located in Zebrzydowa near Zgorzelec/Goerlitz (at the German border). At the same time, Aronia was propagated by seeds and cuttings in the nurseries near Lublin and Kraśnik Lubelski. In 1984 a separate section was organized within the Polish Gardeners Association and named: the National Association of Aronia Producers. This small group of horticulturists united the enthusiasts

Aronia orchards produce fruit every year. Yields vary depending on growing conditions and cultivar but for a typical season they amount to 7 tons from a hectare. Frequently they reach even 10-15 tons. Berries are, for the most part, harvested mechanically. A machine called a shaker sends a vibration through the twigs sufficient enough to cause the berries to fall. They fall onto a canvas where they are sent by a conveyor belt to a box.

of Aronia fruits. They were convinced that Aronia was a plant with a great future, very attractive for industrial horticulture, and the berries were a valuable source material for the food industry. The best Aronia cultivars were selected and, over the years, the experimental stations produced several million seedlings, which enabled the production of Aronia berries on a large scale, and industrial farms now cover thousands of hectares.

It is interesting to note that the cultivation of Aronia was started with much enthusiasm, but contrary to the official opinion of the state-owned Research Institute of Pomology in Skierniewice. The staff of this Institute considered Aronia to be less useful for industrial agriculture. In 1986, at the POLAGRA Polish Agricultural Fairs in Poznań, the producers of Aronia presented their seedlings, Aronia berries and food products for the first time, and the group was awarded gold! It was a success!

But the joy was short. Unfortunately, in the same year (1986), a temporary breakdown of production occurred. It was a consequence of information broadcast on TV, stating that heavy metals accumulate in Aronia. The news was bad and untrue. Actual scientific studies and analyzes showed just the opposite.

Arsenic, lead or cadmium do not accumulate in the fruits of Aronia.

Even when the bushes grow near the highway with heavy traffic, the fruits contain less toxic compounds than the level accepted by the regulations and EU Directives. It is also very important to state:

Aronia does not require chemical protection against pathogens, pests and diseases and therefore fruits do not contain traces of pesticides. It is an ecological type of fruit!

Agropharm S.A., a Polish company in **Tuszyn** near **Łódź** (founded in 1988), manufactured red pigment from Aronia. This natural dye containing anthocyanins could replace synthetic coloring agents used in foodstuffs. In 1991 another company, **Aronia S.A.** from **Leczyca**, introduced Aronia juice to the Polish market. The juice quickly became very popular and was awarded the gold medal at POLAGRA, Polish Agriculture Fairs in Poznan in 1993. At present, the majority of juice manufacturers have Aronia juice amongst their products and the demand for Aronia concentrate increased.

A significant share in the popularization of Aronia has the former Experiment Station of the Research Institute of Pomology in Albigowa near Lańcut. That Station developed industrial farming of fruits, and has been involved in the production of Aronia plants for decades. In its orchards a special genotype of Aronia, named "galicjanka", was selected. This cultivar is characterized by very good fertility, and the berries ripen simultaneously, which is important when using combine harvesters.

In the 1990's intense scientific studies on the biological role of antioxidants were conducted world-wide. These studies showed that antioxidants, mainly flavonoids, are not only important constituents in human nutrition, but can offer significant antiatherogenic, anticancer or anti-inflammation protection. These properties have moved interest from the "antioxidant component" of healthy foods to the "antioxidant, bioactive component" of pharmaceutical preparations.

Agropharm S.A. developed a technology for obtaining dry antho-cyanin-rich extract from Aronia berries. Investigations of its biological and therapeutical properties, carried out at the Military Academy (now Medical University) in Lódź, by Professor J. Niedworok's team, con-firmed that this extract displays health-promoting activity in many diseases of free-radical ethiology. In 2002 this extract appeared on the Polish pharmaceutical market as "Aronox". First results of the clinical tests performed at the II Clinic of Cardiology of the Medical University of Warsaw, showed that the extract lowers blood pressure in the patients with hypertension. It suggests that anthocyanins of Aronia may be useful when applied against athero-sclero-sis(see section 10.2).

Several other studies on the bio-logical activity of Aronia extract gave interesting results, opening new per-spectives for its applications. It appears that its development and use as a food coloring product started an avalanche of possible medical applica-tions. The dyeing is only one, now evidently less important feature of this preparation.

OXIDANTS AND ANTIOXIDANTS

The words **oxidant** and **antioxidant** can now be frequently found in books, reviews and scientific publications.

As we know, the energy needed for living is obtained through a controlled process of oxidation. Chemical reactions of oxidation and reduction accompany all life processes in plants, animals and humans. These reactions have been extensively investigated, but the role of free radicals produced in the cells is not so well understood. Although the first radical was identified in the 1900's, a majority of them live only a fraction of a second and are difficult to detect. A frequently asked question is: **how do these short-living species influence the biochemistry of the cells?** Is it possible to destroy biomolecules in such a short time?

Over the recent years the application of Electron Paramagnetic Resonance (EPR) spectroscopy in biochemistry and medicine has contributed a great deal to the understanding of free radical reactions and oxidative damage to molecules, cells and tissues.

There are at least two interesting books worth reading. One is "EPR in Biochemistry and Medicine", showing how the radicals can be detected in tissues and body fluids of healthy individuals and patients suffering from a variety of diseases[1]. The second one, "Flavonoids in Health and Disease", highlights the major natural antioxidant substances involved in maintaining health and longevity[2]. Although its first sentence states: "oxygen is a dangerous friend", the conclusions are optimistic. Evolution has developed effective antioxidant and antiradical systems. Healthy people consuming enough fruit and vegetables should not worry about free radicals.

Students, keeping in mind some fundamentals of chemistry may skip the following section. Other persons will find the answer to the question: what is a radical?

5.1.
PHYSICOCHEMICAL APPROACH TO ANTIOXIDANTS

Oxidation means a loss of an electron (or an increase in oxidation number), reduction – a gain of an electron. Organic chemistry teaches that oxygenation occurs when the number of oxygen atoms in a molecule increases, or the number of hydrogen atoms decreases. Although there is no one, commonly accepted definition of an antioxidant, its rather useful characteristic was given by professor Halliwell:

"An antioxidant is a chemical compound which, present in small amounts in comparison to the substance undergoing oxygenation, strongly inhibits this process".

It is worth noticing that this definition does not provide any information about the chemical structure of the antioxidant. Antioxidants can vary, but their common feature is their reducing power. However, the properties of a chemical compound strongly depend on its surrounding: the solvent and other solutes. In certain solvents the compound may be effective as an antioxidant and in another behave as a pro-oxidant.

The function of antioxidants is to intercept and react with free radicals at a faster rate than the substrate.

The antioxidant properties of polyphenols can be related to the hydrogen atom abstraction from the OH group. The presence of a strong antioxidant (reductor) seemed to be beneficial. However, in this reaction the phenoxy radical appears (with an unpaired electron at the oxygen atom), exhibiting strong oxidative properties. If the concentration of such radicals increases or they do not recombine sufficiently fast - their action is pro-oxidative.

The groups of antioxidant compounds, as well as, particular representatives are subjected to intensive investigation; their physicochemical properties are tested in the laboratories (*in vitro*) with the aim to predict their behavior in a living organism (*in vivo*).

Professor Halliwell, quoted above, said: "if a chemical compound is a poor antioxidant *in vitro*, you may not expect that it will be much better *in vivo*", and he was right. Unfortunately, frequently the reverse situation occurs: a strong antioxidant, when administrated to laboratory animals, is not biologically active, decomposes in the digestive tract or is not absorbed. It is difficult to predict biochemical pathways and metabolism of a compound *in vivo*. Usually, it is administrated orally, as a component of food, but how and where is it absorbed, metabolized and removed? Pharmacokinetic and pharmacodynamic studies on particular compounds frequently found in fruit are in progress (see section 10.1). The data on bioavailability of flavonoids are desired not only as a lacking part of fundamental knowledge but also for developing functional foods and nutraceuticals.

5.2.
OUR ENEMIES – REACTIVE OXYGEN AND NITROGEN SPECIES

Humans, like other living organisms, need oxygen to produce energy. Everybody knows that without oxygen and breathing, humans can only survive several minutes. However, few people realize that oxygen is a free radical (with two unpaired electrons), and that its excess is dangerous to life.

A free radical is a molecule (or its fragment) with an odd number of electrons (represented as dots near the chemical formula or name, e.g. OH•).

Should we use the name "radical" or "**free radical**"? It is now a historical problem, the name free radical (for example, the methyl radical $CH_3{}^{\bullet}$) is used in order to differentiate this species from a substituent (the methyl group CH_3), also a fragment of an organic molecule. Stable, covalent chemical bonds are formed by a pair of electrons. The odd or unpaired electron seeks to pair with another electron (a recombination reaction); therefore, the radicals are highly reactive and have short lifetimes. Most frequently, there are no other radicals in the neighborhood and the radical reacts with the nearest molecule, starting a chain of subsequent radical reactions. Oxygen-derived free radicals and cascades of other radicals are toxic for cells. The excess production of these radicals is called "**oxidative stress**". The term indicates that the antioxidant status of cells has been changed by exposure to oxidants. During a persisting oxidative stress normal reducing environment inside cells is altered and a depletion of antioxidants occurs. Overproduction of radicals and a weakened defense system result in membrane damage and oxidative DNA damage, both dangerous for the survival of cells.

The progress in the spectroscopic methods, such as the electron paramagnetic resonance (EPR) spectroscopy, enabled the detection and characterization of radical species appearing in many tissues. Much attention was paid to free-radical reactions in the development of pathologies.

As mentioned above, oxygen is a bi-radical, and its molecule in the triplet state should be: $^3O_2{}^{\bullet\bullet}$. In spite of two unpaired electrons it is not a dangerous free radical.

More reactive radicals result from one-electron reduction of oxygen: **superoxide anion $O_2{}^{\bullet-}$**, and its protonated form **hydroperoxyl radical $HO_2{}^{\bullet}$**. Both are produced in mitochondria in a metabolic process: the reduction of oxygen to water. The following reduction step yields **H_2O_2, hydrogen peroxide**. It is a well-known oxidant (its 3% water solution is used as a disinfectant and germicide) although it is not a radical. It is long-lived and may diffuse long distances in tissues since it is a neutral, small molecule. Through the Fenton-type reaction, in the presence of transition metal ions, it may produce the most dangerous radical: **hydroxyl radical OH•**. It is the most reactive among the radical species; its half-life in organism is about 10^{-9}s and the typical rate constants for its reactions are of the order of 10^{10} ($1 \text{ mol}^{-1}\text{s}^{-1}$). It means that it will react within a very short distance from the place of generation.

In the series of one-electron reductions a sequence of products appears:

$$O_2 \rightarrow O_2{}^{•-} \rightarrow H_2O_2 \rightarrow OH^{•} \rightarrow H_2O$$

These processes can be summarized as follows:

$$O_2 + 4e^- + 4H^+ \rightarrow 2H_2O$$

Four electrons are added by an enzyme, cytochrome oxidase, and the electrons and protons have to be transported without disturbances in order to produce ATP (an energy metabolite).

The electron-transporting processes during energy generation are very effective and 98-99% of oxygen is metabolized to the final product – water. However, 1-2% stop at intermediate stages. Thus, $O_2{}^{•-}$ and H_2O_2 appear as by-products of normal metabolism, and are continuously generated by mitochondrial respiration. These $O_2{}^{•-}$ radicals have to be neutralized (scavenged) by endogenous antioxidant systems.

The amount of $O_2{}^{•-}$ produced in the organism of an average woman was estimated as 160-320 mmol ($1 \text{mmol} = 10^{-3}$ mol, M) daily; the organism of a man (weighing 80 kg) produces even more: 215-430 mmol. The concentration of another product, hydrogen peroxide, is 100-1,000 times lower and reaches 10^{-6}-10^{-8} M. The level of H_2O_2 depends on the kind of tissues; it is higher in brain, liver or heart.

The most dangerous radical is OH• (not to be confused with anion OH⁻); it may initiate DNA strand scission, followed by chromosome damage. The oxidative damage to DNA is repaired by enzymes that excise the lesions, and oxidized bases can be detected, for example, in the urine. The number of oxidative hits to DNA per cell per day is about 10,000 (10^4) in the human and 100,000 (10^5/day) in the rat. An old rat has 2×10^6 lesions per day which is evidence that oxidative damage accumulate with age.

Oxygen radicals, molecule of ozone and H_2O_2 are described altogether as: **reactive oxygen species, ROS**. In the free radicals also nitrogen atoms occur, and nitric oxide NO• - recently a very popular molecule in biochemistry – is a free radical; also the peroxynitrite **ONOO**- is highly reactive. These radicals and ions are likewise described as:

reactive nitrogen species, RNS.

Nitric oxide NO$^\bullet$ is well known in medicine as a signaling molecule, but its radical properties are frequently not considered. It can be involved in various reactions: reduction to the anion **NO$^-$** or oxidation to nitrosonium cation **NO$^+$** (it requires the presence of strong oxidants, such as hydroxyl radical OH$^\bullet$ or peroxynitrite anion). Nitrosonium ion NO+ can nitrosate nucleophiles: thiols, amines and aromatics, the final effect is nitrosation or nitrosylation of biomolecules. Excess nitric oxide can react with superoxide radical to produce the very toxic **peroxynitrite anion**:

$$NO^\bullet + O2^{\bullet-} \rightarrow ONOO^-$$

The formed **ONOO$^-$** is a powerful antioxidant under physiological conditions; it induces oxidative damage to tyrosine and tryptophan or proteins containing these residues. Reactions mediated by peroxynitrite, such as oxidation of methionine or base deamination, lead to the irreversible damage to proteins, lipids and DNA and, therefore, a loss of function. Nitrotyrosine in proteins has been detected in atherosclerotic lesions of human coronary arteries, indicating that RNS are generated and involved in the pathogenesis.

Oxygen and nitrogen radicals caused oxidative damage to DNA but also to aminoacids, carbohydrates and lipids. Polysaccharides can be degraded by oxidative attack, likewise the proteoglycans. Polyunsaturated fatty acids are very sensitive to oxidation and the products of such reaction are prostaglandins, prostacyclin and leukotrienes. Unspecific lipid peroxidation gives a number of degradation products, which are involved in the development of atherogenic lesions.

Reactions of radicals with DNA, proteins and lipids and especially the accumulation of their products – damaged biopolymers, is the first step in the progression and eventual development of pathology, leading to disease. The aging process has also been linked to cumulative effects of oxidative stress.

5.3.
BIOCHEMISTRY OF ANTIOXIDANTS

In order to understand how the organism protects itself from oxidation, we should learn something about oxidation and the reduction process, frequently described as redox processes. The redox state of the cell is the balance between the steady-state levels of reactive oxygen and nitrogen species and the cellular antioxidant systems. A variety of components, of both endogenous and exogenous origins, which make up these systems, create an **antioxidant barrier.**

Antioxidant barrier includes small molecule antioxidants (which scavenge free radicals), enzymes (which catalyze quenching reactions) and metal binding proteins (which sequester iron and copper ions).

The diversity of antioxidants apparently extends those few mentioned below, such as:

• **glutathione** (a tripeptide, intracellular GSH is present in mmol quantities; it is not a vitamin because it is synthesized in an organism),

• **uric acid** (final product of purine metabolism, neutralizes free radicals in cytoplasm),

• **ascorbic acid**, known as **vitamin C** (active in water phase, has to be supplied everyday with dietary products),

• **α-tocopherol** or **vitamin E**, (soluble in lipids, protects cell membranes for oxidation).

• **retinol** or **vitamin A** and the carotenoids (protecting lipid rich tissues)

• other important compounds, such as:

▶ **coenzyme Q (ubiquinol)**
▶ **bilirubin,**
▶ **melatonin,**
▶ numerous radical scavengers absorbed from plant foods, and because of that described as **bioflavonoids** or **phytamins (similar to vitamins)**.

The chemical principle behind the protection offered by an effective antioxidant is that it will react with the oxidant before the oxidant will react with any important biomolecules. Non-enzymatic anti-oxidants act mainly as radical scavengers in oxidative chain reactions.

Millions of years of mammalian evolution developed numerous enzymatic mechanisms that keep redox processes under control, remove the excess of free radicals and repair the damages. The essential enzymatic antioxidants are: superoxide dismutases, catalases, glutathione peroxidase, and other hemoprotein peroxidases. They are characterized by specific cellular content, localization and specific form of metal (copper, manganese, iron) or selenium ions involvement.

Structural oxidative damage to organic molecules (DNA, proteins, lipids, carbohydrates) has to be repaired enzymatically. Enzymes involved in DNA repair (nucleases, glycosylases, polymerases, ligases) operate in several ways, such as nucleotide excision, base excision, recombinational repair or mismatch repair. In the absence of cell division, the oxidative lesions are removed from DNA quite effectively and the mutation rate is kept to a minimum. Oxidized proteins are degraded by proteases. Unspecific oxidation of lipids (lipid peroxidation) leads to a number of degradation products removed by phospholipases, transferases or acetyltransferases.

The cellular redox state is related to age and current status of the cell. It appears that cells become more oxidized during the progression of the life cycle. The GSH redox potential (the ratio GSH/GSSG, e.g., reduced glutathione (GSH) to oxidized one with -SS- bridges) and cellular level of H_2O_2 can serve as indicators. In the proliferative state the glutathione redox status is approximately -250 mV and the level of hydrogen peroxide is below 0.7 µM. Apoptotic cells have a redox status of approximately -150 mV, and the level of H_2O_2 increased to over 3 µM.

Oxidative stress is the shift of the redox status of the cell towards oxidation.

The cellular response to oxidative stress can be the enhancement of antioxidant defenses, repair of damage and survival or senescence followed by apoptotic or necrotic cell death. How do the cells communicate and "take decisions"?

The process that transduces the extracellular message across membrane into the intracellular space is called **signal transduction** or **cell signaling**. The components of signal transduction include small molecules as well as macromolecules (proteins): receptors, couplers, messengers, protein kinases and phosphoproteins. Many intracellular signaling proteins behave as molecular switches. The reception of a signal activates them and causes them to pass the signal through the cell, after which they can be switched off until another signal is received. Molecular switches are activated by phosphorylation or activated by the binding of a guanine nucleotide (G- proteins).

Oxidation - reduction reactions also regulate signal transduction (**redox signaling**).

Oxidants: ROS and RNS under sub-toxic conditions are now realized as signaling molecules.

Redox signaling can be mediated by $O_2^{•-}$, H_2O_2, $OH^•$ and lipid hydroperoxides[3]. ROS induce gene expression by stimulating Ca^{2+} signaling and protein phosphorylation.

It seems that some amounts of radicals are necessary!

Several ligand-receptor interactions produce ROS and the antioxidants block receptor-mediated signal transduction; it suggests that ROS may be second messengers for transcription factor activation, apoptosis, cell growth or chemotaxis.

A well-studied redox signaling mediator is nitric oxide. Its appearance changes antioxidant status of the cell since it is a free radical (generated by nitric oxide synthases); $NO^•$ acts as the second messenger for important physiological processes: smooth muscle relaxation, neurotransmission, platelet inhibition and immune regulation. Mitogen-activated protein kinase (MAPK) signaling pathway seemed to be influenced by NO[•] and flavonoids[4]. Both, flavonoids and NO[•] may directly influence oxidative/nitrosative stress or act within MAPK signaling cascades creating a feedback loop.

Oxidative stress contributes to neurodegenerative disorders, including Alzheimer's disease, Parkinson's disease and neuronal loss associated with the age-related cognitive decline. However, the damage to biomolecules as the result of oxidative stress appears to be too simplistic a picture since it ignores stress response mechanisms that cells have developed. Accumulating evidence indicates that the MAPK signaling cascades are involved in neuronal survival, regeneration and death.

Recent epidemiological and dietary intervention studies suggest that flavonoids (Ginkgo biloba, green tea extracts or pure flavonoids) may prevent neurodegeneration or cerebral ischemia/reperfusion injuries.

It might be speculated that flavonoids exert their neuroprotective effects independent of their classical antioxidant properties and interact with proteins of signal transduction pathways.

A different interpretation of potential bioactive effects of flavonoids might be the up-regulation of antioxidant enzymes, such as SOD, catalase, and glutathione peroxidase.

Flavonoids: flavonols and anthocyanidins are very potent NO[•] scavengers. Nitric oxide radical has beneficial effects (produced by endothelial cells leads to muscle relaxation in blood vessels), but also undesirable effects (generated in excess by inflammatory cells is toxic). The anthocyanidins, cyanidin and pelargonidin, appeared to be more potent scavengers of NO[•] than rutin and hydroxyethyl rutosides (a rutoside mixture is administrated to reduce capillary permeability and has anti-inflammatory activity).

The half-life of NO[•] decreased by 50% by adding only 5 μM pelargonidin, the most potent compound studied[5]. The NO[•] scavenging potency correlates with the therapeutic efficacy.

The reactivities of twelve major anthocyanins identified in bilberry extracts towards nitric oxide (NO[•]) and peroxynitrite (ONOO-) were studied[6] in vitro using capillary zone electrophoresis. The reactivities of the anthocyanins towards NO[•] were slightly weaker compared with that of (+)-catechin as a reference antioxidant under anaerobic conditions, except delphinidin glycosides (Dp-3-glys). The reactivities of other anthocyanins were not significantly affected by either the aglycone structure or the type of sugar moiety. Under aerobic conditions, all anthocyanins and catechin showed significant enhancement of the reactivity, indicating that they reacted with other reactive species generated secondarily. Dp-3-glys showed rather extraordinally high reactivity towards ONOO- compared to other anthocyanins.

Accumulating evidence suggests that the cellular effects of flavonoids may be mediated by the interactions with specific proteins central to intracellular signaling cascades and independent of their antioxidant capacity. Flavonoids can act at phosphoinositide 3-kinase (PI 3-kinase), tyrosine kinases, protein kinase C and MAP kinases[7]. Inhibitory or stimulatory actions at these pathways are likely to affect cellular function by changing the phosphorylation state and by modulating gene expression.

An important question to answer is: are the polyphenolic compounds only hydrogen-donating antioxidants or also cell signaling molecules?

Polyphenols are not only antioxidants; they may exert beneficial or cytotoxic actions through their modulation of signaling cascades (MAP kinases). Understanding of their signaling mechanism of action is crucial to the evaluation of biological activity.

Flavonoids and their metabolites may participate directly in antioxidant reactions in plasma by scavenging ROS and RNS, but the concentrations are low, lower than those of vitamin C or E. Among the compounds contributing to antioxidant

barrier, only the glutathione is present in milimolar quantities; the concentration of flavonoids are of the µmol (10^{-6} M) or even of nmol (10^{-9} M) order.

Flavonoids are extensively metabolized *in vivo* and the bioactive forms (glucuronides, sulphates, O-methylated derivatives, flavonoid-GSH adducts) are not the same as found in plants (glycosides and aglycones).

Besides direct reaction with radicals, flavonoids may also protect cells from various insults by other mechanisms. Many flavonoids may protect neural cells from glutamate toxicity and oxidative injuries. The mechanisms of protection included: acting as antioxidants, directly affecting GSH metabolism and maintaining low Ca^{2+} levels despite high levels of ROS. The mechanism is highly specific for each compound. In general, the more hydrophobic a flavonoid is, the more protective it is against glutamate toxicity. A hydrophobic antioxidant may easily enter the cytoplasm where ROS are generated[8].

All described mechanisms (and many others) protect the human body well from oxidative (nitrosative) stress and there is redox homeostasis in the cells. In the young and healthy organisms enzymatic processes function without disturbance.

How long are we young, healthy and protected by nature?

The evolutionarily programmed time for effective defense is limited to ca. 40 years and includes growing up, maturity, procreation and taking care of the next generation. There is no reason to invest in the post-repro-ductive phase of life.

The free-radical hypothesis of aging states that progressive accumulation of macromolecular oxidative damage is the fundamental underlying cause of senescence and pathologies.

The duration of life is a function of genetically determined constitution and the average rate of metabolism. It is known as the "rate of living" hypotheses; the duration of life varies inversely to the rate of energy expenditure. The available data tends to favor the view that oxygen consumption entails the generation of reactive oxygen species and the increased production of ROS is the primary factor responsible for aging.

We do not want to age and die so early! Many persons think that "real life begins when you are over 40" when the children are grown up and leave home. In any case, we decide to do everything in order to live in full health.

5.4.
HOW TO LIMIT THE SOURCES OF FREE RADICALS?

Scientists agree that an important risk factor, supplying free radical directly to the lungs, is **cigarette smoke**. Besides oxygen radicals, it also contains nitric oxides (and the well-known molecule NO•, also a radical). Make every effort to quit cigarette smoking, avoid sitting in rooms or cafeterias full of smoke (passive smoking). The same reason is valid for car combustion gases, but avoiding them is difficult when living in the cities.

Another important factor, producing free radicals, is **UV radiation**. The sun continually produces UV radiation: UV-A and UV-B rays reach the earth and are a major cause of skin damage like sunburn, immune suppression, aging and even skin cancer. Radiation from the UV range has enough energy to disrupt chemical bonds in a molecule. The damaging biomolecules absorbed by human skin include: collagen, lipids. The two popular ways of protecting the skin are: applying a sunscreen lotion to the exposed areas or simply covering the skin with a garment. Conscious individuals will add skin cream with flavonoids and

Recipe for healthy years "50+":

• **daily intake of suitable amount of dietary antioxidants**

• **avoiding situations connected with overproduction of free radicals**

• **being an optimist!**

consume more fruit and vegetables.

Long sunbathing at the seashore, in the high mountains or frequent visits to Solaria (especially without the cream with respective protection filters and without a diet rich in antioxidants) are not beneficial to our skin. Exposure to UV accelerates aging processes!

If the pathogens – **bacteria or viruses** - enter the organism, its reaction is immediate: phagocyte cells (macrophages, monocytes, granulocytes) are sent to fight with infection. The defense mechanism involves the production of antioxidant mixture: $NO^{•}$, OCl^-, H_2O_2, $O_2^{•-}$, destroying proteins and membrane lipid of pathogens. Free radicals and reactive species are not selective and their reactions induce oxidative damage of surrounding tissues. The defense involves costs. It is difficult to avoid infections completely, but long lasting infections and chronic inflammations should not be neglected, they should be carefully cured.

There is now a growing body of evidence suggesting that **intensive physical exercise** can itself cause damage by means of the increased "oxidative stress" - the consequences of a hugely increased oxygen consumption by the working muscles and the body as a whole (exercise involves a 10-20-fold increase in the whole body oxygen consumption and a staggering 100-200-fold increase in the local muscle oxygen consump-

tion). All endurance activity is associated with oxidative stress, and the higher the intensity of the exercise, the greater the stress. However, regular performance of exercise generates an adaptive response that helps to protect the body against the effects of such stress.

Constant psychological stress can make people sick, and the researchers try to find its underlying biochemical mechanisms. They discovered that the neurotransmitter glutamate plays a role in the neurodegenerative pathway and believe that accumulation of glutamate and related amino acids in the brain triggers oxidative stress and neurotoxicity. Blood tests showed that Interleukin-6 (IL-6) sharply increased in the blood of the stressed people compared with the blood of the others in the test. Previous studies have associated IL-6 with several diseases, including heart disease, arthritis, osteoporosis, type-2 diabetes and certain cancers. Rising levels of the stress hormones – cortisol, adrenaline and noradrenaline – also lead to increased oxidative stress.

Humans are designed to have a strong survival instinct and to be able to respond to life-threatening situations. However, when we stay in that "mode" without a break for months or years our body starts to fail.

All living under psychological of physical (athletes) stress might expect to benefit from a diet rich in antioxidant vitamins found in:

• Green leafy vegetables, particularly broccoli, spinach and cabbage

• Root vegetables including onions, carrots and potatoes

• A wide range of fruits, including berries like Aronia, cranberry, blueberry

• Vegetable and fish oils and wholegrain cereals.

It is worth pointing out that a diet deficient in overall calories is unlikely to maintain an adequate antioxidant defense - we need energy to maintain metabolic processes. **However, the rate of energy utilization determines the rate of aging!**

The support for the "rate of living" hypothesis has been provided by such assays as a decrease in body temperature (down to hiber-

nation), mutational inactivation of enzymes, and decreased level of physical activity. For instance, the elimination of flying activity prolongs the life span of flies up to 3-fold and the DNA oxidative damage is correspondingly diminished. Among mammals, decrease in the rate of oxygen consumption and body temperature are widely employed physiological mechanisms of adaptation to scarcity of food. A calorie-restricted diet significantly increases the lifespan of rodents (rat, mouse) and also decreases reproduction. Darwinian fitness in animals seems to increase by the delay of the reproductive function during periods of hunger; the saved resources are invested in maintenance of the body.

Lowering the rate of metabolism, meals with less calories and protein arm food slows down aging processes.

How much should we eat? The association between the energy intake and mortality was examined in a large epidemiological study of Japanese-American men. The diet of 1,915 healthy non-smokers, aged 45-68 years at the onset of the study, was followed for 36 years. Applying the adjustment for age and other confounders, there was a trend toward lower mortality in the second quintile of energy intake, suggesting that men who consumed 15% below the group mean were at the lowest risk of the all-cause mortality (increased mortality was seen with intakes below 50% of the group mean).

The observed trends between low energy intake and reduced risk for all-cause mortality in humans should not be considered as encouragement for prolonged fasting. It is an invitation to some restrictions... Perhaps one could consume a glass of fruit juice and a cup of berries instead of calorie-rich dinner?

Currently, scientists are looking for the strong, natural antioxidants between compounds isolated from plant material. Plants have to protect themselves from excess UV radiation, oxygen and pathogens and therefore they have developed a chemical defense system.

The synthesized compounds include polyphenols, such as tannins, anthocyanins, and flavonols.

Humans ate plant foods directed by instinct and tradition. At present, we have a support from biochemistry and food chemistry. The decision to increase consumption of spinach, broccoli or berries has scientific background.

Recognition of the antioxidant barrier of plants, and its utilization for maintaining or improving human health are actual challenges for food and medical sciences.

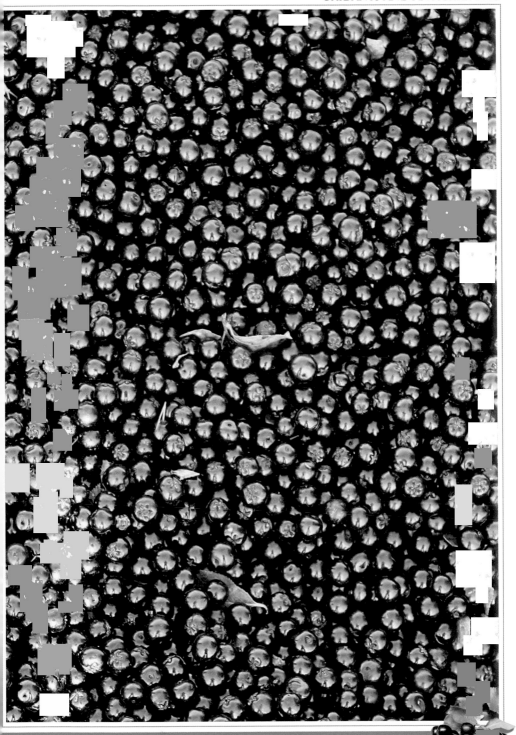

ANTIOXIDANTS IN PLANTS

Most plants contain an array of polyphenolic compounds, mainly flavonoids. They are considered as secondary metabolites. Why are they produced? In the last decade our ability to isolate these compounds from plants and to determine their structures has improved with the progress in analytical techniques. Accumulated information has resulted in a better understanding of the distribution of flavonoids in the flowering plants and the role these compounds can have in insect-plant interactions, pollination, seeds dissemination, UV protection and the defense against herbivores.

The concentration of flavonoids in plant cells often exceeds 1mM, their metabolic pool is rather static but the synthesis of many phenolic compounds is greatly affected by environmental stresses. Very often the synthesis of additional pigments is induced by: UV light, temperatures, drought, wounding or pollutants. Red anthocyanins are abundant in juvenile and senescing leaves and ripening fruits.

6.1.
FLOWER COLORS - HOW TO BE BLUE AND ATTRACTIVE TO POLLINATORS?

Discovering the linkages and relationships between the kingdom of plants and animals is a fascinating job. New concepts frequently result from curiosity-driven research and answering some simple questions. Such as, why flower petals are so colorful (orange, red, scarlet, magenta violet or blue)? Why is the petal's color so important?

One of the best-established functions of flower color and the subsequent production of pigments is the provision of color attractiveness to pollinators. Modern analytical methods enabled the detection and identification of these pigments; they appeared to be flavonoids, anthocyanins, frequently anthocyanin-flavone complexes or complexes with metal ions. Anthocyanins are glycosides of anthocyanidins; most popular anthocyanidins are: cyanidin (Cy), delphinidin (Dp), malvidin (Mv), peonidin (Pn), petunidin (Pt) and pelargonidin (Pg) (see section 7.3). The color results from the chemical composition of these dyes. However, why does a plant synthesize several or even several dozens of such compounds?

The color of flower petals results from an interplay between the plant and its pollinator. The blue flower color is the preferred attractant of bee pollinators, so that evolution towards blue is apparent in temperate plants in the areas where bee pollination is dominant. The primitive plant families have red flowers and anthocyanins with cyanidin (like Rosaceae, especially genera Rose). Blue flowers of several plant species have been studied in detail and delphinidin was found as the most common anthocyanidin in these plants.

Petunia integrifolia, Petunia hybrida

Petunia flowers – glycosides of petunidin can be found in its petals!

Pelargonium – its flower petals contain glycosides of pelargonidin

Popular petunias (*Petunia integrifolia, Petunia hybrida*) have been bred since 1830's and the flowers of modern cultivars span almost all of the colors. The relative floral anthocyanin contents of almost 200 commercial petunias were determined and the presence of five major anthocyanidins (Cy, Dp, Mv, Pn, Pt and Pg), occurring as glucosides, rutinosides, sophorosides or gentiobiosides, were detected.

The flowers of pelargonium (*Pelargonium domesticum*) vary in color from white through pink, orange, red to purple (blue is missing). While either flavonols or carotenoids are responsible for cream/yellow coloration, all other colors resulted from anthocyanin mixes. Physicochemical studies attempt to understand color variation through an investigation of structure, composition, concentration, and anthocyanin pigment/copigment ratio.

Physicochemical explanation: Maxima of light absorption for delphinidin glycosides at ca. 535 nm are nearer the blue region (580 nm) than the maxima of cyanidin glycosides, which appear at ca. 525 nm. Therefore, in order to shift the maximum to blue, delphinidin derivatives should be preferred.

The analysis of chemical constituents of petals confirmed that delphinidin is associated with the blue and mauve flower color, malvidin with mauve to purple, cyanidin with magenta, and pelargonidin with pink and orange.

Pelargonium domesticum

The "shift to blue" can be achieved by copigmentation with flavone or flavonol, intermolecular interactions, complexing metal cations (Fe, Mg, Al). Cyanidin- or pelargonidin-based pigments are less effective in their production of blueness, because they require more flavone copigment.

6.2.
PROTECTION AGAINST SUNLIGHT

During very hot days animals and humans prefer to stay in the shade. Plants cannot run and therefore have evolved their own defense mechanisms. They have to survive under strong solar radiation, in spite of the fact that only a fraction of this energy is necessary for photosynthesis. Amongst three UV bands: A, B and C, the UV-B is the most dangerous to life on the Earth's surface.

Ultraviolet-B radiation is the band of 280-315 nm wavelengths and of the high energy; it can penetrate the stratosphere and cause damage to plants. Continuous depletion of the stratospheric ozone layer resulted in an increase in UV-B radiation. In addition to the Antarctic ozone hole, ozone depletion has also been discovered in the North Polar Region as well as in Northern and Southern midlatitudes. Biologically active doses of UV-B penetrate deep into water, and may also affect the aquatic ecosystem. A number of processes in plants, such as photosynthetic oxygen production and CO_2 uptake are susceptible to UV-B, thus influencing their growth and survival.

Excess of UV radiation results in biomass reduction, decrease in pollen germination and reduction in photosynthetic activity. Since photosynthetic organisms in their natural habitat are simultaneously exposed to visible and UV radiation, they have to develop mechanisms counteracting the damaging effects of UV. Besides the repair of the UV-induced damage of DNA by excision and synthesis of UV absorbing/screening substances also the accumulation of antioxidants and antioxidant enzymes takes place. Antioxidants provide protection by scavenging harmful radicals or oxygen species and reduce oxidative stress in plant cells.

A series of experiments have provided convincing evidence that plants subjected artificially to UV-B radiation respond by changes in the pathway of flavonoid syntheses: the production of polyphenolic-type compounds increases. Amongst them are: flavonols, catechins and anthocyanins, absorbing UV radiation in the 280-315 nm range.

The degree of DNA damage caused by UV-B radiation was measured on two cultivars of corn: purple leaved and green leaved. The purple strain with anthocyanin did not suffer the induction of the DNA damage produced in the green form[10]. Anthocyanin pigment of maize leaves presumably is able to provide UV-B protection like other flavonoids do, although the UV absorption of anthocyanins is around 280 nm. An interesting experiment was performed on Scots pine *Pinus sylvestris*.[11] Flavonoids increase in concentration after a UV-B treatment; the quercetin glucoside induced in cotyledonary needles reached 0.8-0.9 µMol/g and the major flavonoid, kaempferol glucoside in primary needles accumulated to reach a maximum of 2.4 µMol/g f. wt.

Changes upon radiation have been observed not only in the leaves but also in the levels of flavonoids in the leaf wax. Flavonoids, which absorb in the 280-315 nm region, are capable of acting as UV filters, thereby protecting the underlying photosynthetic tissues from damage.

The fruit of two apple cultivars, differing in their ability to produce anthocyanins when exposed to sunlight, has been analyzed by reflectance spectroscopy.[12] Apples (*Malus domestica*, cultivars Antonovka and Zhigulevskoe) were collected in the botanical garden of the Moscow State University. Although the formation of anthocyanins in apples is a genetically determined process, their biosynthesis depends on light intensity. Considerable amounts of anthocyanins are accumulated in red sun-exposed sides of Zhigulevskoe fruit, whereas the shaded sides of both cultivars are pale green. The red color of apple is attributable to cyanidin-3-galactoside (idaein). In both cultivars the reflectance spectra showed absorption bands between 350 and 700 nm; apple anthocyanins possess an absorption band at 500-600 nm with a maximum near 550 nm. To obtain additional evidence for the photoprotective role of anthocyanins, the fruits were illuminated using a light source of 400-700 nm, i.e., from photosynthetically active radiation. Anthocyanins considerably increase light absorption by apples and show more stability to irradiation than chlorophylls. The experiments revealed high resistance of anthocyanins in apples to prolonged irradiation but the precise mechanism of stability *in vivo* is not clear yet. Anthocyanins in aqueous solutions, *in vitro* are known to be sensitive to photochemical degradation.

It is remarkable that anthocyanins exert a strong effect on light absorption in the band of 500-600 nm, exactly in the gap between the chlorophylls and carotenoids absorption bands, close to the solar energy peak. It seemed that the protective effects of anthocyanin pigments against light-induced stress are due to their functioning as an internal light trap for solar radiation.

A beautiful, red apple anthocyanin pigments accumulate in the light-exposed surface

There are grounds to believe that (because of vacuolar localization) anthocyanins in plants are not involved in free radical reactions in chloroplasts. It is more likely that their photoprotective effects are due to the light screening, filling the chlorophyll absorption gap in the green-orange part of the visible spectrum.

It is obvious that light starts photosynthesis, but it acts also as a signal inducing secondary metabolite production. Many biosyntheses of secondary metabolites by plant cell suspension are enhanced by light irradiation. Light-enhanced production requires special photosensory and photoregulation systems.

The experiments on strawberry cells showed that anthocyanins production depends not only on light intensity and light quality (blue light enhanced anthocyanin biosynthesis, whereas red light hardly affected it) but also on the light/dark cycle operation. Anthocyanin is synthesized through a dozen reaction steps, where several enzymes (such as chalcone synthase) are activated by light, and a lag-time is necessary for their activation. Anthocyanin production was not stopped by transferring cells to the dark for several seconds only. It suggests that light-activated state is reduced by a kind of turnover. Cryptochrome, a blue light photoreceptor, seems to be related to anthocyanin biosynthesis in strawberry cells. The light-activated state of cryptochrome may be kept for several seconds in the intermitted dark. In the hour-scale cycle, continuous light operation enhances the production of anthocyanin more than the light/dark cycle process. Such information is valuable for designating photo bioreactors for enhanced anthocyanin production.

Vitis vinifera cells synthesize high levels of anthocyanins when they are cultured in a polyphenol synthesis-inducing medium. After adding ^{13}C-phenylalanine to the culture medium, its uptake was complete and the accumulation of anthocyanins in grape cells was stimulated. Using Vitis vinifera suspension cultures maximal rate of ^{13}C enrichment anthocyanins reached 65%. The production of ^{13}C-labelled anthocyanins is necessary to solve the problem of their pharmacokinetics and bioavailability in humans[14]. The ^{13}C isotope is not radioactive, the nuclei are characterized by the magnetic moment and can be observed by Nuclear Magnetic Resonance Spectroscopy (NMR). Unfortunately, its abundance is 1.1%, therefore ^{13}C-enriched compounds are easier to detect in body fluids (plasma, urine or saliva).

6.3.
DEFENSE AGAINST PATHOGENS AND HERBIVORES

One of the functions of polyphenols, especially flavonoids is their role in protecting the organism against microbial invasion. They are present in plants and are also rapidly accumulating in response to attack.

The flavonoids are also recognized as effective antifungal and antiviral agents. Experiments in vitro show, that numerous flavonoids are effective antifungal, antibacterial and antiviral agents. Baicalin, a flavonoid obtained from the roots of Scutellaria baicalensis appear to have direct inhibitory activity of human immunodeficiency virus (HIV), a causative agent of AIDS[15]. Quercetin and also other flavonols are active in the inhibiting of tomato ringspot virus, interfering probably with an early event in the virus life cycle[16].

Insects feeding on plants are sensitive to flavonoids present in the leaves; flavonol glycosides can be phagostimulants or feeding deterrents. Isoflavones of clover are feeding deterrents to the beetle *Costelytra zealandica* that attacks the roots of legumes. Danaid female butterfly *Danaus plexippus* is attracted for oviposition by a mixture of flavonol glycosides present in the leaf of *Asclepias curassavica (Asclepiadaceae)*.

The role of flavonoids, especially proanthocyanidins and tannins, in defending plants from herbivores is far from understood but some interesting facts can shed some light on these relationships. The rapid synthesis of bitter tannins could act as defense against herbivores, employed by grass and trees. The high level of tannin in the plant material contribute to the astringent bitter taste, since tannins interact with salivary proteins. This reaction is known as "tanning" and has been applied for centuries in the leather industry.

Studies on monkey feeding in Africa indicated a significant rejection of high-tannin containing plants. Chimpanzees appear to tolerate much higher doses of tannins in the diet but eating leaves they select young ones with lower tannin levels and reject the tannin-rich seeds when eating fruit of wild figs.

In some summers the population of lemmings, small rodents, increases rapidly. In their natural habitat, the grass on meadowland starts to protect itself by producing tannins and becomes uneatable. Hungry animals desperately try to find a new habitat, and swim across rivers and lakes. It looks like a loss of self-protecting instinct. The rodents die in spite of the green environment.

Some herbivorous mammals developed an adaptation to a diet containing condensed tannins by production of proline-rich proteins in the saliva. These proteins bind tannins and the complex passes through the stomach without causing any harm. This is an adaptation to winter-feeding, and then they eat the bark and twigs of trees. The moose from Scandinavia and North America produce condensed tannin-binding proteins in the saliva. It is worth noting that these proteins do not bind hydrolysable tannins and the animal cannot eat those plants which have both types of tannins.

CHEMISTRY OF ARONIA FRUITS

Water is the main component of all fruit; in the second place we find sugars. Ripe fruits of Aronia have 74-83% of water and 17-26% of dry mass, circa 10% of fresh fruit mass are sugars.

The sweet taste and pleasant smell (owing to the presence of etheric oils) make fruit so widely liked; it is a commonly accepted constituent of the diet. It was widely accepted that health benefits of fruit consumption result from the content of vitamin C. It is true: the majority of fruits contain significant amounts of vitamin C, some have also β-carotene (pro-vitamin A) and other carotenoids. Currently, this opinion can be revised: health benefits of the fruit-rich diet result from the content of polyphenols: flavonoids, caroten-oids, vitamin C and numerous other ingredients. In fruit there are more important compounds that just vitamin C!

7.1.
VITAMINS AND PHYTAMINS

Most vitamins were discovered in the 1930's. It was found that there are some necessary constituents of foods, soluble in water (vitamin C and vitamins B) and in lipids (vitamins A and E), which cannot be synthesized by a human organism.

The term "vitamin" is derived from the words "vital" and "amine", because vitamins are required for life and were originally thought to be amines. Although not all vitamins are amines, they are organic compounds required by humans in small amounts in the diet. An organic compound is considered a vitamin if a lack of that compound in the diet results in overt symptoms of deficiency.

The subsequently discovered compounds were denoted with further letters of the alphabet. The sequence was not followed to the last letter "Z" but there were numerous candidates, fulfilling the definition. Progress in analytical methods resulted in dramatic increase in the number of chemical compounds isolated from plant food as well as from medicinal plants. These compounds are "biologically active" because they are consumed, absorbed and they participate in metabolic processes.

The life and vitality of human beings depend on vitamins, certain minerals and hundreds of other compounds. Their role and biochemical reactions are not fully recognized, but their deficiencies in the daily nutrition can be devastating for health.

Organic compounds from plants, required by a human organism in small amounts are called phytamins, like vitamins (the majority are not amines).

Phytamins are sometimes called "**vitamins of the New Millennium**", and the most important compounds are polyphenols. Polyphenols have one or more OH groups linked to aromatic ring (phenol contains only one OH group). Amongst polyphenolic compounds are flavonoids: flavonols, flavanols, anthocyanins, catechins and its dimers or trimers (called procyanidins) and high molecular mass polymers - tannins (hydrolysable and condensed) as well as phenolic acids.

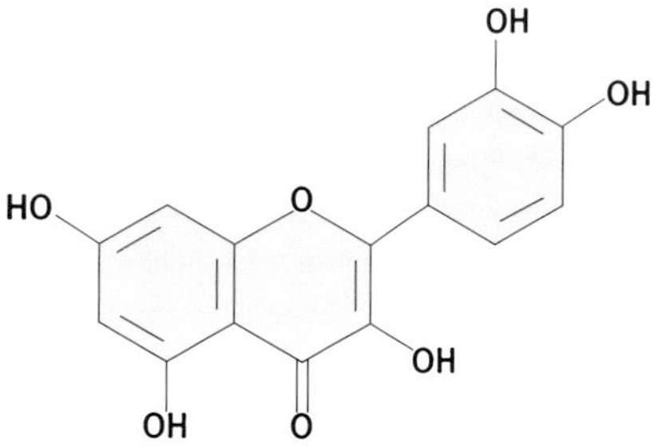

Quercetin

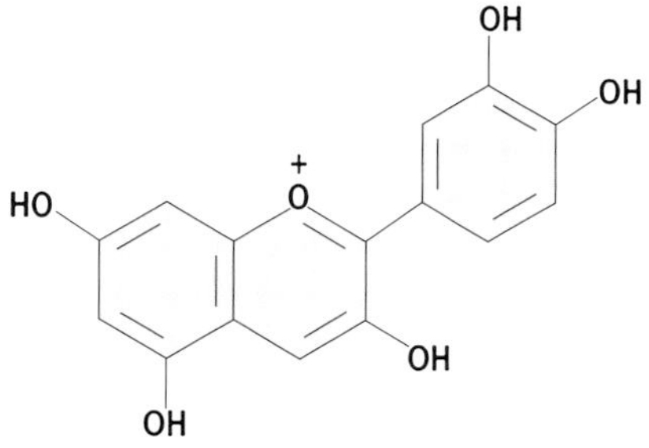

Cyanidin (flavylium cation)

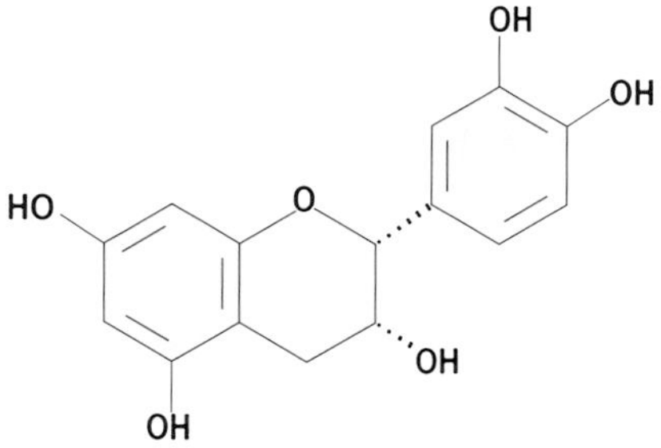

Epicatechin

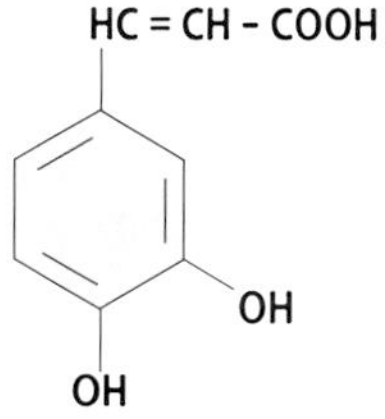

HC = CH – COOH

Caffeic acid

Fig. 1. Chemical formulas of polyphenols from different groups: cyanidin (anthocyanidin), quercetin (flavonol), caffeic acid (hydroxycinnamic acid), epicatechin (flavan-3-ol).

7.2.
FRUIT POLYPHENOLS

Consumption of fruit and vegetables is associated with a lowered risk of cancer, heart disease or ischemic stroke. One possible reason for this protection is the presence of vitamins C, E and the pro-vitamine β-carotene in fruit. However, supplementation studies with pure vitamins have cast doubt on this issue. Other dietary components, polyphenolic antioxidants, for example, flavonoids are reported as protective as vitamins and more efficient. Many phenols and polyphenols are stronger antioxidants than the vitamin antioxidants, favorably affect the serum antioxidant capacity and protect against lipid peroxidation. Conclusion: we have to follow a fruit and vegetable-rich diet.

Unfortunately, only 9-17% of Americans consume the recommended five servings of fruit and vegetables daily. It was of interest to measure the quantity and quality of the phenols present in commonly consumed fruits in the American diet. In general, sweet fruits are preferred. Comparing the fruits on the basis of serving size a very large difference was observed: from 55 g for cranberries to 286 g for watermelon. Eight fruits: banana, apple, grape, watermelon, pear, cantaloupe, peach and strawberry provide 86% of the daily phenols. Bananas provide the largest percent contribution (32%) to the per capita consumption of fruit phenols.

However, the berries had the highest levels of antioxidants among the fruits and provide the largest amount of valuable polyphenols according to serving size.

Looking at consumption per capita (g/day) it is clear that cherries, blueberries, cranberries and grapes are underutilized in an average American diet. Berry fruits, which are commercially cultivated and consumed in fresh and processed forms in North America, include blackberry (*Rubus spp.*), black raspberry (*Rubus occidentalis*), blueberry (*Vaccinium corymbosum*), cranberry (*Vaccinium macrocarpon*), red raspberry (*Rubus idaeus*) and strawberry (*Fragaria ananassa*). Blueberries and cranberries are harvested in Nova Scotia, Prince Edward Island or North Carolina. Other berry fruits, which are lesser known but consumed in the traditional diets of North American tribal communities, include chokecherry (*Prunus virginiana*), highbush cranberry (*Viburnum trilobum*), serviceberry (*Amelanchier alnifolia*), and silver buffaloberry (*Shepherdia argentea*). Taking into account the biological and physiological functions of these "superfoods" and their potential impact on human health, the dissemination of this information to the general public is necessary.[18]

In the North European countries (Norway, Scotland, Finland) domestic berries, both wild and cultivated, are consumed in abundance because other fruits are not grown in the northern climate. Berries have long history in folk medicinal uses, now their potential health benefits are intensively studied. In Finland, berries are part of the traditional diet. Compositional data on phenolic compounds in berries has been rapidly accumulating and included in the national food composition database. Among the different bioactive substances in berries, phenolic compounds including flavonoids, tannins, and phenolic acids have received considerable interest. Tannin-containing berries exhibit antimicrobial properties against pathogenic bacteria, thus offering many new applications for food industry. Berries and berry extracts became widely utilized as food supplements.

The knowledge of the phenolic composition is essential to evaluate the importance of berries as a source of bioactive compounds. Berries are rich in flavonoids and phenolic acids. Fresh berries can have up to 100 mg/kg flavan-3-ols (catechins), up to 200 mg/kg hydroxycinnamic acids as well as, a high content of anthocyanins (5000 mg/kg). Significant variations in the polyphenolic profiles between different berry and different berry cultivars have been found. Increased maturity at harvest results in higher anthocyanin and the total phenolic content in Vaccinium species. Both varietals and regional differences in the flavonol and phenolic acid content were found in 26 berry samples collected in Finland. The inspection of the data in Table 1 shows significant differences in phenolic content.

Table 1. Content of polyphenols in purified berry extracts (in mg/100 g dry weight).

Fruit	Anthocyanins	Flavonols	Hydroxycinnamic acids	Total polyphenols
Aronia mitschurini, Viking	1,041	79	422	4,210
Bilberries Vaccinium myrtillis	2,298-3,090	54-130	113-231	3,300-3,820
Black currant Ribes nigrum	756-1,064	72-87	58-93	2,230-2,790
Cranberry Vaccinium oxycoccus	397	200	147	2,200
Raspberry Rubus ideaus	172-298	15-30	23-27	2,730-2,990
Strawberries Fragaria ananassa	184-232	10-20	47-63	1,600-2,410

Previous studies usually determined the total phenolics content in fruit and berries. Later, intensive studies on particular phenolic constituents in berries have been conducted. In the extracts of raspberry (*Rubus idaeus*), bilberry (*Vaccinium myrtillus*), black currant (*Ribes nigrum*), strawberry (*Fragaria ananassa*), chokeberry (*Aronia mitchurinii Viking*), cranberry (*Vaccinium oxycoccus*), rowanberry (*Sorbus aucuparia*) and apple (*Malus pumila*), phenolic profiles have been determined using analytical chromatography (HPLC). The contribution of six groups of polyphenols: anthocyanins, flavonols, flavanols, hydroxycinnamic acids, elagitannins and procyanidins to the antioxidant activity of the berry extracts have been estimated.

In *Vaccinium* species anthocyanins are the major phenolic subgroup, in strawberry and red raspberry ellagitannins predominated (in raspberries ca. 1.7 g/100 g of dry weight of the extract). In the berries belonging to the family *Rosaceae* the content of hydroxycinnamic acids was relatively high, compared to that of berries from other families. In rowanberries hydroxycinnamic acids, chlorogenic and caffeic, prevailed (679 mg/ 100 g), and in Aronia 422 mg/100 g was found.

Significant differences in phenolic profiles were detected among berry samples from different harvest years, as well as in various cultivars. It is difficult to distinguish between the factors causing the differences.

However, the effect of light on the phenolic metabolism can be noticed. The increase in solar radiation results in higher contents of phenolics, especially anthocyanins in berries. Also low temperatures may increase anthocyanin accumulation.

Interestingly, those wild berries that grow in unfavourable conditions:
- **in the cool northern climate**
- **under a short growing season**
- **exposed to strong UV-vis radiation (long days, white nights)**
- **without fertilizers, pesticides or herbicides have high phenolic contents compared to cultivated berries grown in the mild climate.**

Fresh berries are, of course, the most favorable and important source of polyphenolic compounds. However, in northern countries fresh fruits and berries are available only in the summer and they have to be preserved, dried, frozen etc. for winter months. Pressed juice from berries and small fruits may be fermented to obtain fruit wine. The berry wine-making process is the same as making wine from grapes; berry wines and liquors are produced industrially in some countries (e.g. cassis form black currant, cherry liquor). Berries and fruits such as cherries, black and red currants or elderberries are used to produce wine for domestic use in European Union countries (Germany, Sweden, Finland, Poland).

The purpose of the study performed in Finland[22] was to evaluate the antioxidant activity of 44 berry and fruit wine and liquors. Total phenolic contents ranged between 91 and 1,820 mg/L, and no significant correlation with the relative antioxidant activity (methyl linoleate oxidation measurements) was found. The wines made from mixtures of black currants and bilberries (and of black and red currants) showed the highest antioxidant activity and were slightly superior to the reference red grape wine. The raw materials contain phenolic compounds capable of protecting lipids against oxidation also in hydrophobic lipid systems, thus suggesting potential benefits in attempts to utilize berry products as foods. The very strongly colored berries such as bilberries or black currants are the richest in anthocyanins and exert high antioxidant activity.

A popular way of preservation is also preparing an infusion of berries steeped in alcohol (tinctures). Are these products valuable and do they contain bioactive phenolic compounds?

In 1990-2003, different research groups studied extraction methods for berries to produce phenolic extracts with a high antioxidant activity. Using pure water at room temperature resulted in low yields of phenolic compounds compared to mixtures of water and alcohol or water and acetone. Anthocyanins and other phenolic compounds are better soluble in the aqueous mixtures with ethanol or methanol than in pure water. Therefore, with 60% methanol the yields of anthocyanins extracted from bilberries is two times higher and total phenolics even three times higher than with water. The data illustrated in Fig. 2 were obtained with methanol but similar results could be achieved with ethanol.

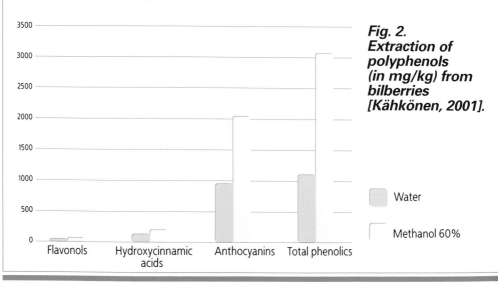

Fig. 2. Extraction of polyphenols (in mg/kg) from bilberries [Kähkönen, 2001].

Table 2.
Content of biologically active compounds in Aronia berries harvested in Poland [the data from the Faculty of Biotechnology and Food Sciences, Technical University of Łódź]

Compounds	Content in mg/100 g fruits
Anthocyanins	• 480 (dry) • 240 (frozen)
Flavonoids	• 107 (dry) • 12.2 (frozen)
Tannins	• 6.3 (dry) • 1.8 (frozen)
Pectins	• 300-600
Sugars	• 6.6-10% (fresh) • 32.3-42.8 % (dried)
Organic acids, Vitamin C	• 1.1-1.35% • 14-28 mg
Carotenoids	• 4.86
Minerals	• 550-800

To treat fruits or berries with alcohol is a common method of preparation of domestic alcoholic beverages. Our predecessors should be appreciated: 40% ethanol (vodka) is a properly adjusted extraction mixture and the fruit extract is rich in polyphenols, the procedure was established hundreds years ago without modern analytical equipment and biochemical studies. The alcoholic extract is stable, it can be kept in a dark place for months and the content of alcohol protects it against mold or bacteria.

The recognition of chemical constituents of Aronia berries is the merit of Professor Jan Oszmiański from Poland, and the first report[23] on the content of anthocyanins in Aronia was published in 1988. The investigations of tannins of Aronia and chlorogenic/neochlorogenic acids[24] were performed in the laboratory of the Agricultural University in Wrocław. Chemical components of Aronia berries were interesting for scientists from the Technical University of Łódź, Poland, since the knowledge on the constituents is essential in the choice of manufacturing procedure. The aim of these studies was to develop the technology of production of Aronia juice, wine and spirit[26].

On average, **Aronia fruits can have up to 10-20 g polyphenols in 1 kg, and the content of anthocyanins may reach 4.0-8.5 g in 1 kg** (according to American data, from the University of Illinois).

The dominating organic acids are: chlorogenic and neochlorogenic, malic, tartaric and citric; because of their presence, the pH is low: 3.3-3.8 inside berries – it hinders bacterial invasion (and facilitates transport and storage of Aronia crops).

Aronia fruits also contain useful minerals and microelements, such as: (in mg/100 g): potassium (27), calcium (14), phosphorus (8), iron (1.2), copper (0.2), manganese (0.7) and zinc (0.5).

It is interesting to compare Aronia with other fruits, which are more popular in Europe such as blueberries, bilberries or cherries.

The data collected in Table 3 clearly indicate that **Aronia is the leader among other fruits and berries with the highest content of anthocyanins and total polyphenols**.

7.3.
ANTHOCYANINS OF ARONIA

Polyphenolic compounds in plant materials have been widely studied, most works concentrated on flavonols (quercetin, kaempferol and their glycosides) and flavan-3-ols (catechins). Anthocyanins, have received less attention than other flavonoids, in spite of the fact that their consumption can be much higher. In the USA diet the intake of anthocyanins was estimated as 180-215 mg daily whereas the intake of flavonols (calculated as quercetin) was only 23 mg.

The name **anthocyan** is a combination of two Greek words: anthos - flower and kyanos - blue; and was used for the first time in 1835.

Anthocyanidins – (aglycones) are polyphenols and **anthocyanins** are glycosides (anthocyanidins linked to sugars). Sugar (glucose, rhamnose, xylose, galactose or arabinose) is most frequently attached at C3; the position of this attachment could be also 7, 5 or 3', 4', 5'.

To date, there are 17 known naturally occurring anthocyanidins, and more than 400 anthocyanins have been found in plants. Six anthocyanidins are common in higher plants (their distribution is given in parentheses): cyanidin, (50%), pelargonidin (12%), peonidin (12%), delphinidin (12%), petunidin (7%) and malvidin (7%). The characteristic feature is that *in vitro* at a pH of 3, or lower, the anthocyanidins are red and exist as flavylium cation:

Table 3. Polyphenols in fruits, in mg/100g fruit (data from the Faculty of Biotechnology and Food Sciences, Technical University of Lódź[27]; for comparison, data from German studies[28] given in parentheses.

Fruit	Total polyphenols	Anthocyanins	% of anthocyanins in polyphenols
Aronia	2080	505 (300-630)	24.3
Elderberry		(450)	
Bilberry		(160-500)	
Strawberry	225	45 (28-70)	20
Black currant	560	140	25
Red currant	210	29	13.8
Sour cherry	460	65	14.1
Red grapes		(8-390)	
Gooseberry	200	-	-
Apple (Jonathan)	250	-	-

Anthocyanins are soluble in water and in polar solvents, such as alcohols. They can be extracted from different plant materials such as, flow-

R3'

OH

HO

R5'

OH

OH

Formula of anthocyanidin

R3'	R5'	Anthocyanidin
H	H	Pelargonidin
H	OH	Cyanidin
OH	OH	Delphinidin
OCH_3	OCH_3	Malvidin
OCH_3	H	Peonidin
OCH_3	OH	Petunidin

er petals or fruits using methanol or ethanol with small admixture of acid. Acidic medium stabilizes cationic form of anthocyanins.

Discussing the distribution and properties of anthocyanins in the academic books, the reader is usually informed that anthocyanins are present in nature in very small amounts. Their role is limited to colorant (red, orange or blue) of flower petals.

A much higher concentration of anthocyanins can be found in fruits; it is particularly high in the dark soft

fruits and berries. Anthocyanins are present in the outer part of the hypoderm, which can be immediately recognized as a dark deep color. The names of fruits are informative, as well: black currant, blackberries. An especially high content of anthocyanins is found in chokeberry – its ripe berries are almost black. The Aronia juice has a beautiful dark-red color, similar to that of red wine. On the basis of fresh weight of fruit, the chokeberry has a significantly higher anthocyanin and phenolic content than other berries and fruits.

Aronia berries have an intense dark purple color.

Aronia is one of the richest natural sources of anthocyanins,

containing from 300 to 630 mg anthocyanins in 100 g of fruit, typically ca. 500 mg. Aronia berries contain ca. 100 mg more anthocyanins than elderberries and much more than black currants.

In the anthocyanin fraction isolated from Aronia berries cultivated in

Poland four anthocyanins have been found with only one aglycone cyanidin; the sugars: galactose, glucose, arabinose and xylose are linked at C3. The dominant anthocyanin is cyanidin-3-O-galactoside (60%); cyanidin-3-O-arabinoside is also a major constituent and the presence of cyanidin-3-O-xyloside in berries is rather unique.

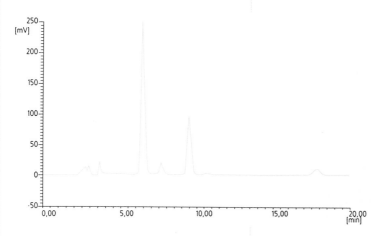

Figure 3.

The HPLC profile of Aronia anthocyanins (in commercial extract from Aronia, Aronox), detection at 520 nm. The highest peak represents Cy-3-gal, next peaks on the right: Cy-3-glu, Cy-3-ara and Cy-3-xyl.

Anthocyanins differ in the substitution pattern of the aglycone moiety and in sugar units (or sugar chains). Fruits and berries have a characteristic profile of anthocyanins, and the contribution of individual compounds can change in different species and cultivars; it depends also on maturity, harvesting time and place. Anthocyanin profiles enable fast identification of fruits or berries.

Investigations of the anthocyanin pigments from the grape skin showed that the anthocyanin pattern is characteristic of the cultivar. The typical anthocyanin "fingerprint" changes during vinification, maturation and aging, and the illegal improvements of the wine color can be identified using HPLC. The classification of 52 different German wine samples was performed by the multivariate statistical analysis and the authentic wines of the different varieties and origin can be separated.[29] The characteristic pattern of anthocyanins from red wine Cabernet Sauvignon is illustrated in Fig. 4; the anthocyanins are mono- or diglucosides of five anthocyanidins (Dp, Cy, Pt, Pn, Mv) and esters of the glucose part with acetic, p-coumaric or caffeic acid. The dominating anthocyanin (over 50%) is malvidin-3-O-glucoside (Mv-gl).

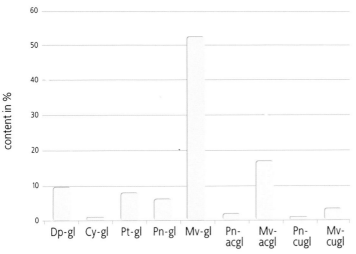

Fig. 4.

Anthocyanins in wine (Cabernet Sauvignon): glucosides (gl), acetylglucosides (acgl) and coumarylglucosides (cugl); major anthocyanin is malvidin-3-0-glucoside [Berente, 2000]

Usually the fruits contain a mixture of anthocyanins with one or two dominating. The characterization of such a mixture involves the separation and collection of each compound and subsequent analysis by NMR and mass spectrometry (MS).

The profile of anthocyanins of cranberry and chokeberry is illustrated in Fig. 5, for comparison. Among anthocyanin constituents of cranberry (*Vaccinium macrocarpon*, Ben Lear) peonidin-3-O-galactoside (Pn-gal) is the dominant compound (27.3%), followed by peonidin-3-O-arabinoside (Pn-ara) (12.7%).

Cyanidin-3-O-galactoside and cyanidin-3-O-arabinoside are the dominant anthocyanins in chokeberry (*Aronia melanocarpa*). In the wild American chokeberry (from Jonesboro, ME) more cyanidin-3-O-arabinoside (Cy-ara) than cyanidin-3-O-galactoside (Cy-gal) has been found: 1424 micrograms of Cy-ara and 1,256 micrograms of Cy-gal, expressed as Cy-glu equivalents per gram of fresh weight.

In Aronia berries cultivated in Poland there is more Cy-gal than Cy-ara, as it was determined by Oszmiański [Oszmiański, 1988] and confirmed at the Medical University of Warsaw (see Fig.3).

In the red grapes, cranberries and blueberries there are sugar derivatives of five anthocyanidins (Cy, Pn, Mv, Pt and Dp), whereas in cherries, black currants and Aronia only one agly cone has been found – cyanidin (Cy).

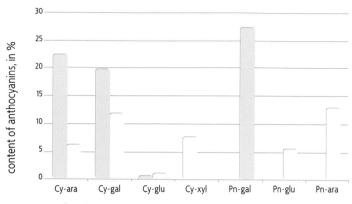

Figure 5.

The content of anthocyanins in the fruits of American Aronia and cranberry [Zheng, 2003]

Aronia
Cranberry

Anthocyanins and anthocyanidins are not stable; they easily undergo structural transformations resulting in color loss. The factors affecting degradation include: higher temperature, increased pH, exposition to oxygen and light, the presence of ascorbic acid, sugars, enzymes, metal ions and others.

Compounds appearing at higher pH: colorless carbinol pseudo-base (pH 4-5), purplish quinoidal base (pH 6-7), yellow chalcone (pH 7-8) are depicted in Fig.6.

At low pH red flavylium cation dominates. As the pH is raised, the hydration reaction of the flavylium cation gives a colorless carbinol pseudo-base, which can undergo ring opening to chalcone pseudo-bases. The proton transfer reactions related to acidic OH groups give rise to purplish quinoidal bases. Further deprotonation of the bases can take place at pH values between 6 and 7, with the formation of quinoidal anions. The heating of the anthocyanin in solution accelerates their transformation to chalcones, and further oxidative reactions lead to the appearance of some brown degradation products. The exposition to oxygen and storage at higher temperatures results in the browning of the fruit or flowers, as is frequently observed during drying of plant materials.

Decomposition of anthocyanins in fruits occurs under the influence of enzymes oxidases, catecholase and laccase. Aronia contains a lot of polyphenolic compounds with ortho-dihydroxy groups, e.g., (-)-epicatechin and its polymers or the derivatives of caffeic acid, these compounds are sensitive to the action of catecholase. Laccase is active in fruit affected by mold; therefore during the processing of fruits the pulp should be rapidly heated to inactivate oxidative enzymes.

Never use the fruits with mold for processing nor mix them with the untouched ones. Not only would the color be changed to brown but the mold would also produce carcinogenic mycotoxins.

Fortunately, chokeberries contain compounds with antimicrobial and antifungal activity, such as benzoic acid, sorbitol and catechin polymers. These berries are more resistant to microbial invasion than other fruits.

Anthocyanins of Aronia are rela-

tively stable and the stabilizing factor is a low pH of berries (3-3.8), the presence of chlorogenic acid and also catechin-anthocyanin linkages.

Anthocyanins undergo condensation reactions forming polymers similar to condensed tannins. With increasing polymerization anthocyanins and procyanidins become more difficult to dissolve in aqueous media. It leads to the precipitation of anthocyanin-procyanidin polymers (in stored Aronia juice concentrate).

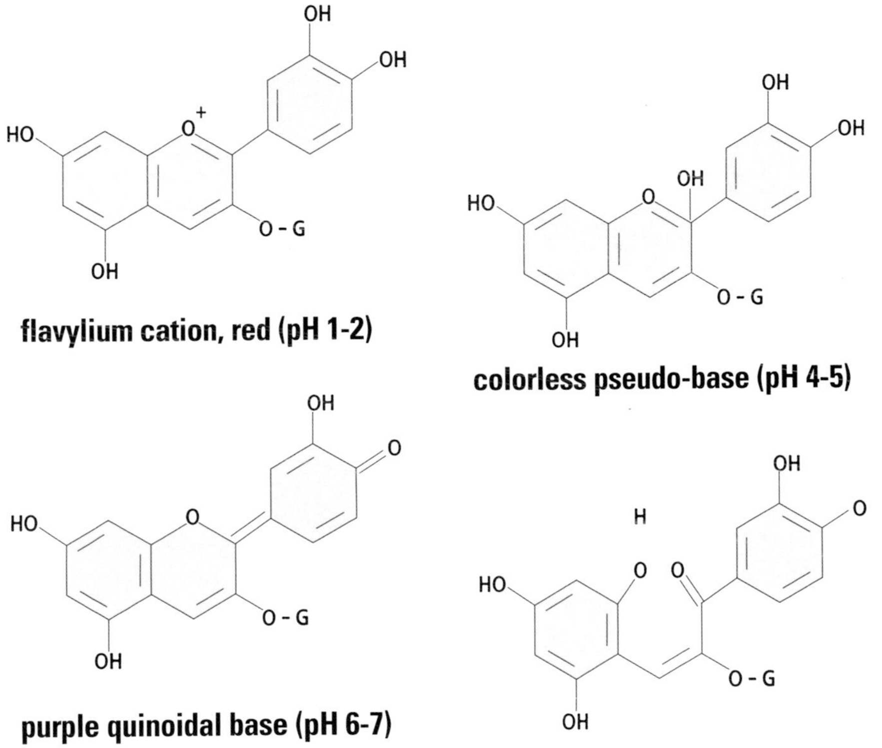

flavylium cation, red (pH 1-2)

colorless pseudo-base (pH 4-5)

purple quinoidal base (pH 6-7)

yellow chalcone (pH 7-8)

Figure 6.
Chemical structures of compounds appearing at higher pH: colorless pseudo-base (pH 4-5), purple quinoidal base (pH 6-7) and yellow chalcone (pH 7-8).

The color brought about by a given anthocyanin mixture can be influenced by intermolecular and intramolecular associations (hydrogen bonding), metal-complexation and the solvent.

Usually, one type of antioxidant dominates in a particular fruit; the simultaneous presence of high amounts of anthocyanins and tannins is a unique feature of Aronia berries.

7.4.
CATECHINS AND TANNINS OF ARONIA

Tannins are high molecular polymers composed of flavan-3-ol units (condensed tannins) or galloyl-glucoses, derivatives of gallic acid (hydrolysable tannins).

Condensed tannins with catechin or epicatechin units are called procyanidins (proanthocyanidins) and such compounds are present in significant amounts in Aronia berries.

Tannins occur in common foods including fruits and vegetables. Lower molecular weight procyanidins are usually present in plant tissue in relatively low concentrations compared to that of larger oligomers (2-10 units) and polymers (more than 10 units).

Tannins act as a defense mechanism in plants against pathogens and herbivores and generally induce a negative response when consumed.

These effects can be an instantaneous astringent, bitter or unpleasant taste. They give Aronia fruits the special hardness of drying up the mouth; the effect is described already by the name "chokeberry". Astringency is the sensation caused by the formation of complexes between tannins and salivary glycoproteins.

Therefore, fresh Aronia fruits are not suitable for consumption. The juice of Aronia produced from concentrate contains sugar and is tasty; the same concerns jams and other sweetened products.

The studies on the chemical composition of tannins in Aronia were conducted by Oszmiański [Oszmiański, Kucharska, 1995]; the results indicated that monomeric or dimeric catechins as well as high-molecular tannins are present.

Polymeric catechins (tannins) of Aronia are built-up with molecules of (-)-epicatechin. Their content is high (over 1.5%), significantly higher than in other berries (60-times higher than in elderberries). The mean polymerisation degree was determined as 70, which is a relatively high value. For comparison, in the tannin fraction isolated from grape seeds and analyzed using the same method, the degree of polymerisation amounted to 18.6.

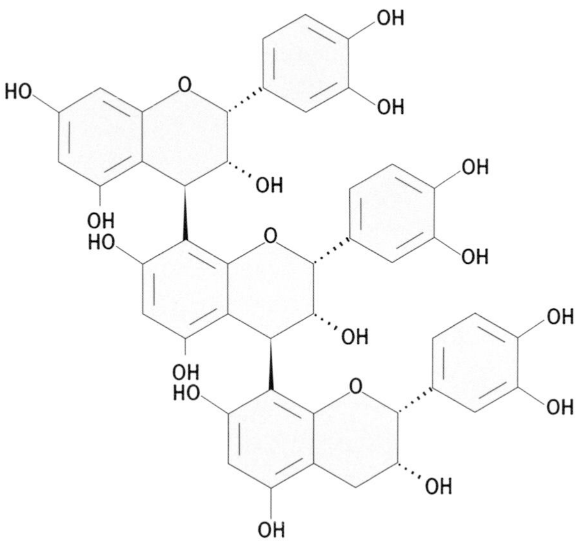

Figure 7.
A trimer composed of epicatechin units

products has been analyzed by HPLC and cyanidin was identified by comparison with the standard substance. The presence of catechin-anthocyanidin polymers has been suggested from the inspection of UV spectrum, absorption at 280 nm is stronger than in the vis-range and maximum of absorption is shifted to the longer waves (526 nm).

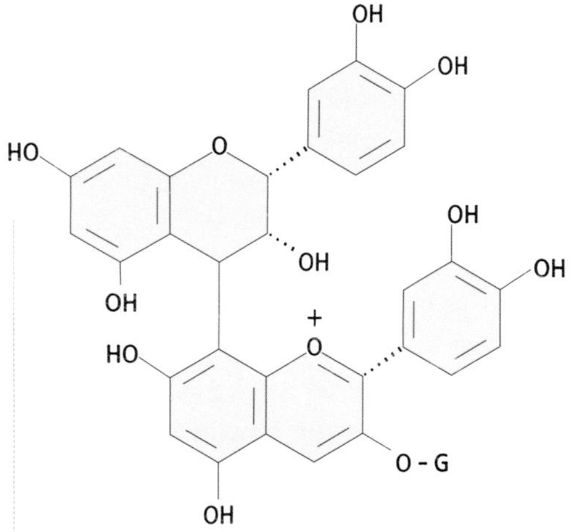

Figure 8.
The structure of dimeric anthocyanin flavan-3-ol (4→8) cyanidin-3-O-galactoside.

The degree of polymerisation for the polymeric procyanidins can be determined by thiolysis. In this reaction, all the extension subunits of procyanidins are attacked by benzyl mercaptan to form benzylthioethers and the terminal unit is released free. After thiolysis the extension and terminal units can be distinguish by HPLC analysis. Thiolysis was employed to characterize the procyanidin fractions obtained from blueberry and cranberry[31].

It is interesting to note that polymeric procyanidins of Aronia are colored – rose. Performing the subsequent thiolytic degradation Oszmiański [Oszmiański, Kucharska, 1995] obtained smaller fragments of tannins and free anthocyanidin dye. The composition of the reaction

The existence of mixed anthocyanidin-epicatechin dimers (see Fig.8) can be confirmed by analysis of ^{1}H and ^{13}C NMR spectra of Aronia pigments; the structure of such compound 4α-8)-cyanidin-3-O-β-galactopyranoside, since the linkage was between C4 and C8 carbons.

Besides Aronia berries, dimeric antho-cyanins linked to flavan-3-ols were isolated from strawberries[32]. The major anthocyanin of strawberries is pelargonidin-3-O-glucopyranoside, fol-lowed by several minor anthocyanins. The UV-vis spectra of the pigments showed two absorption maxima at 516-520 and 432-438 nm and dimer-ic flavonoids containing one antho-cyanidin unit linked to catechin/epicat-echin moiety were separated and analyzed by LC-MS and NMR.

The presence of anthocyanidin in the form of flavylium cation may explain why the condensed procyani-dins of Aronia are soluble in water; higher polymers without cyanidin or sugar units are insoluble and probably not absorbed in the intestine.

• Due to the presence of several OH groups, **procyanidins exhibit antioxidant and antiradical activity, stronger that that of vitamins E and C**.

• Procyanidins form complexes with metal ions and may neutralize toxic heavy metals (Pb, Cr, or Cd) and alkaloids (berberine, strychnine, papaverine).

• Procyanidins have been reported to have **antimicrobial, antiviral, anticancer, anti-inflammatory, anti-allergy** and **anti-hyperten-sive** properties.

• Procyanidins play a protective role in the development of atherosclerosis and cardiovascular diseases and improve platelet aggregation.

• Procyanidins react with collagen, a major structural protein, protecting and supporting the softer tissues, thus exhibiting capillary strengthening properties.

The high content of procyanidins and tannins protects Aronia berries against microorganisms and mold and the fruits can be stored longer. Procyanidins linked to anthocyanins are probably better absorbed. However, there are no studies on the bioavailability of such compounds.

7.5.
PHENOLIC ACIDS AND OTHER COMPOUNDS

Besides anthocyanins and procyani-dins, the polyphenolic constituents of berries also include phenolic acids: hydroxybenzoic and hydroxycinnamic ones. The total content of organic acids in Aronia berries was deter-mined as 1.1-1.35%, including: malic (0.61%), tartaric (0.35%), citric (0.12%) and succinic. Their presence results in low pH: 3.3-3.8; it preserves the growth of bacteria and enables longer storage of Aronia fruits.

In comparison with other berries, Aronia contains significant amounts of biologically active hydroxycinnamic acids: chloro-genic (35.5 mg/100 g) and its iso-mer neochlorogenic acid (21.5 mg/100 g). [Oszmiański, Sapis, 1989].

Chlorogenic acid, an ester of caffeic acid and quinic acid, is widely occurring in plants and many foods (coffee, tea, apple juice). Its role and reactions in humans is now being intensly studied.

It is an antioxidant and metal chelator. The presence of two *ortho* hydroxyl groups enables complexation of metal ions, and iron chelation has been studied in detail.

Chlorogenic acid is easily absorbed and only small amounts are present in urine, indicating that it is metabolized by the liver. It exerts inhibitory effects of carcinogenesis in the large intestine and liver, and has anti-nitrosating properties (may suppress nitrosamine formation in the gastric compartment). Chlorogenic acid can be used as an anti-infectious active ingredient as it has wide anti-virus and anti-bacteria effects with relatively low toxicity and few side effects.

Frequently, the lack of quantitative data on the metabolites hinders the proper evaluation of the potential biological effects of dietary phenols *in vivo*. The aim of the study[35] performed in 2003 was to identify and quantify the metabolites of chlorogenic acid, quercetin-3-rutinoside and black tea polyphenols in humans, and determine the site of metabolism. Healthy humans participated in a dietary controlled crossover study. Their urine was collected and analyzed. Sixty potential phenolic acid metabolites were identified and quantified in urine. Half of the ingested chlorogenic acid and 43% of the tea phenols were metabolized to hippuric acid. The colonic microflora converts most of these dietary phenols into metabolites that then reach the circulation.

Chlorogenic acid and caffeic acid are effective antioxidants *in vitro*, and might therefore contribute to the prevention of several diseases (e.g., cardiovascular ones). Metabolites of dietary phenols show a lower antioxidant activity than their parent compounds; therefore, the contribution of dietary phenols to the antioxidant activity *in vivo* might be lower than expected from *in vitro* tests.

The *in vivo* experiments using obese, hyperlipidemic and insulin resistant Zucker rats showed that fasting plasma cholesterol and triacylglycerols decreased by 44% and 58% respectively after intravenous infusion (5 mg/kg) of chlorogenic acid. Infusion significantly lowered the peak response to a glucose load, and this decrease may be indicative of an improved sensitivity to insulin[36]. Significant differences in the plasma, liver and spleen concentration of selected minerals were also found in chlorogenic acid-treated rats. Chlorogenic acid has been proven, in animal studies *in vitro*, to inhibit the hydrolysis of the glucose-6-phosphate enzyme. This mechanism allows chlorogenic acid to reduce hepatic glycogenolysis and to reduce the absorption of new glucose. In addition, *in vivo* studies on animal subjects have demonstrated that the administration of chlorogenic acid lessens the hyperglycemic peak resulting from the glycogenolysis. The studies also confirmed a reduction in blood glucose levels.

These results suggest that Aronia, rich in chlorogenic acids, may be recommended to diabetics (see section 10.6).

Chlorogenic acid can be used as an antioxidant able to scavenge nitrogen and oxygen radicals, its oxidation in the presence of glutathione and tyrosinase gave mono-, di- and tri-glutathionylochlorogenic acids[37]. It suggests that in the cells chlorogenic acid may react with glutathione, which is one of the most important intracellular antioxidants.

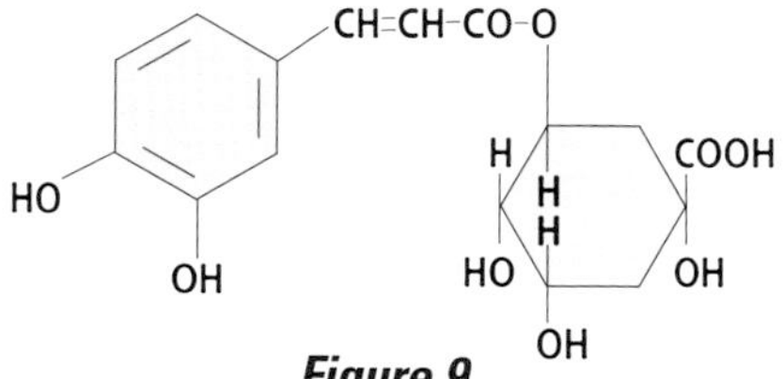

Figure 9.
The chemical formula of chlorogenic acid, a representative of hydroxycinnamic acids, it contains caffeic acid (with aromatic ring) and quinic acid units.

Since the use of synthetic pigments in foodstuffs is not accepted in many countries, the use of natural ones, derived from plants is a far better choice. German scientists from Heidelberg University[38] considered anthocyanins as interesting, natural coloring agents. Anthocyanins can be found in black currants, elderberries or Aronia and their industrial preparation is easily carried out by absorption onto Amberlite XAD. The concentrate, when derived from chokeberries, contained anthocyanins and condensed tannins as the principal constituents, and other low molecular compounds. It seemed worth it to isolate some of them. Therefore the anthocyan concentrate was acetylated (peracetates more easily crystallize), and the peracetylated compounds: glucopyranose, glucopyranosyl benzoate, sorbitol and amygdalin could be identified by NMR and by comparison with authentic samples. Besides them, two hinterto unknown compounds tetra-O-acetyl β-D-glucopyranosyl-pentan-2-one and hepta-O-acetyl (2-pentanyl)-β-D-gentiobioside were isolated. The occurrence of sorbitol and parasorboside is characteristic of the genus *Sorbus*, as a result of which the Aronia plant could be named *Sorbus melanocarpa*, in accordance with chemotaxonomy.

The pleasant smell of Aronia fruits is a result of a mixture of volatile compounds, mainly of the ester type, of which over 20 have been identified. The analysis of volatile compounds was performed using gas chromatography coupled to mass spectrometer (GC MS) and such compounds as:

• esters: ethyl isobutyrate, isoamyl acetate, methyl benzoate,

• alcohols: isoamyl, benzyl and 2 phenylethanol,

• aldehydes: salicylic and benzoic,

• terpenic compounds: carvol, linalool, have been identified.

The qualitative and quantitative composition of carotenoids of Aronia was determined by HPLC[39] in 1989; nine carotenoids were detected: three carotenes (lycopene, ξ-carotene, β-carotene) and six xanthophylls (neoxantin, *trans*- and *cis*-violaxanthin, 5,6-epoxylutein, lutein, β-cryptoxantin).

Fruits of Aronia contain, β-carotene (16.7 mg/kg) and β-cryptoxantin (12.2 mg/kg) as main components; total carotenoids of Aronia were considerably lower than those in *Rosa rugosa* or *Rosa canina* (rose hips) and reached 48.8 mg/kg of non-deseeded berries.

DIETARY ANTIOXIDANTS

The importance of oxidants; free radicals and reactive oxygen species to biological systems has been recognized for some time. If their reactions had the possibility of processing unchecked then the result is a structural change of proteins, inhibition of enzymatic activity, and interference in the regulatory functions and even cell death. Fortunately, nature developed defense systems, endogenous antioxidants: macromolecular, enzymatic ones (like superoxide dismutase, SOD) and non-enzymatic. Non-enzymatic systems include compounds with antioxidant properties such as vitamins E and C, carotenoids, flavonoids and other small molecules derived from plants. Dietary fruits and vegetables are the principal source of antioxidants and consumption of plant-derived products appears to be of great importance.

The diet-related health problems, particularly in highly industrialized nations, suggest that many humans are not eating in a manner compatible with their biology. Anthropoids, including all great apes, take most of their diet from plants, and there is a general consensus that humans come from a strongly herbivorous ancestry. Overall gut anatomy and the pattern of digestive kinetics of extant apes and humans are very similar. Analysis of tropical forest leaves and fruits routinely consumed by wild primates shows that many of these foods are good sources of hexoses, cellulose, hemicellulose, pectic substances, vitamin C, minerals, essential fatty acids and protein.

In general, relative to body weight, the average wild monkey or ape appears to take in far higher levels of many essential nutrients each day than the average American or European, and such nutrients are being consumed together in their natural chemical matrix.

Thus, the recommendation that Americans and Europeans consume more fresh fruits and vegetables in greater variety appears well supported.

8.1.
PLANT EXTRACTS – ROLE IN PREVENTION AND THERAPY

Why are we so keen to popularize the preventive and therapeutic applications of Aronia? One can frequently hear, lets forget these astringent berries; leave them for birds and some amateurs. Let them be eaten by those people who love their specific bitter taste. In the case of illness – we have effective synthetic drugs or have to develop new ones. Why use berries for therapeutic purposes? It could be a witch-doctor practice, or the influence of postmodernism and New Age philosophy.

Humans not only consumed plant foods but also used plants as medicines. All great civilizations utilized plants for the treatment of diseases.

To take an example, the reconstruction of the *materia medica* of the medieval and Ottoman Levant was performed, spanning approximately 1,100 years. Medical and pharmacological literature, travelogues, geographical and agricultural literature, dictionaries and archives revealed that the region was a source of production and marketing of medicinal substances; 234 species of plants, 27 species of animals, and 15 kinds of minerals. The main reason for this is the geographic location of the Levant as a junction between three continents, as a cultural meeting point and as a trade center. Ethnopharmacolgy and archeopharmacology investigating medicinal traditions of the world have already obtained some spectacular findings in this field.

Throughout time, man has discovered, by trial and error, the efficacy of various plants in alleviating human diseases. Many of the plants discovered by primitive medicine men have been investigated by western trained medical personnel and found to be effective.

It was not until the 19th century that man began to isolate the active principles of medicinal plants. Chemists learned to artificially reproduce these active substances in the laboratory. Modern medicine gradually became more and more separated from the natural plant world.

Recently, investigators have returned to the study of the plants and are discovering that the use of the plants in treating illness may be more beneficial than the use of extracted or synthetic ingredients applied in isolation.

It is interesting to note that over 50% of the top twenty drugs could be linked to natural product research. In recent years the development of biological testing systems has lead to the high throughput screening; even 50,000 tests, performed robotically, can be run per day. The major screens for biological activities of plant extracts have been carried out in the search for new anticancer, antiviral and antifertility drugs.

At the end of the 20th century plants have been treated not as a source of natural bioactive compounds but as a source of information on bioactive compounds.

Chemical synthesis of bioactive compounds allowed preserving wild plants in their natural environment. Pharmaceutical companies are now independent from weather or distant transport of raw materials. An interesting chance for cheaper production of valuable chemicals is now created by biotechnology.

The isolation of some natural products (digoxin, morphine, quinine) has resulted in replacing the plant extract with a single bioactive compound. However, sometimes there are advantages to the use of plant extract. The best example might be Dragon's blood, used for treatment of wounds. This red sap is obtained from the bark of South American *Croton* species and its major constituents are polymeric anthocyanidins, followed by diterpenes and simple phenols. The sap forms a protective occlusive layer, simple phenols act as antimicrobial agents, and other compounds exert anti-inflammatory effects.

Large numbers of the world's population use natural plant medicines because synthetic drugs are either not available or too expensive.

However, it is more interesting that in developed countries of America and Europe, herbal remedies have proved to be popular as alternative or complementary treatments of diseases. This tendency is frequently followed by the consumption of natural unprocessed foods and "a healthy way of life".

Conventional medicine has problems with treating chronic diseases since long-term administration of synthetic drugs may cause side effects. The disappointed patients ask if medicine can really cure a disease or only remove the symptoms. An ironic comment goes further, stating "All drugs are poisonous but sometimes have some positive side-effects". Since the biochemical mechanism action of numerous drugs is not well established, it is obvious that medicinal chemistry has a lot of work to do.

The routine treatment of modern medicine; prescribing tablets for the most common health problems have been challenged recently. A new guide devised by the British Medical Journal (BMJ), admits that often the best treatment is no treatment at all. In some cases the doctor should simply say he or she cannot recommend any treatment because there is no good evidence that anything works.

Thus, it seems reasonable to use functional foods, nutraceuticals, and herbal medicinal products in order to strengthen the immune system.

Are these herbal products effective and safe? The European Health Product Manufacturers Association (EHPM), the European Responsible Nutrition Alliance (ERNA), the European Dietetic Food Association (IDACE), the European Food Industry Federation (CIAA) and other organizations watch the market and influence national and international regulations. In 2002 the European Union adopted a Directive on Food Supplements. The institutions and EU member states consider that vitamins and minerals as well as herbal products need to undergo scientific assessment in order to establish recommended intakes and safety.

With the growing body of scientific evidence that supports the potential benefits of taking higher levels of some nutrients, people will take dietary supplements to maintain good health and to decrease the risk of certain illnesses.

8.2.
EPIDEMIOLOGICAL STUDIES

Is an antioxidant-rich diet really necessary for human health?

It could be proven, but not directly. Humans cannot be treated like mice; one group obtains fruit and vegetable and another does not. Short experiments could be accepted but are not so informative, longer experiments would not be accepted for ethical reasons as potentially harmful.

It has happened that the studies planned for several years have been shortened because the control group without supplying vitamins or other important ingredients of the food matrix was in a worse health condition.

Epidemiological studies can be conducted because people have individual food preferences, there are persons not consuming vegetables or neglecting medical indications. Large differences occur between the winter and summer diets. Central and eastern European countries tend to have relatively high incidence of degenerative diseases probably because fruits and vegetables are scarce during the winter and spring, when the typical diet consists of meat, carbohydrates and fat. Nutritional parameters and markers of oxidative stress were studied in three Slovak population groups: 46 survivors of myocardial infarction, 48 healthy citizens of Bratislava and 70 rural controls living according to the traditional life style in a country town. Vegetable consumption in summer/autumn was twice as high as in winter/spring and the biomarkers of oxidative stress followed the periods of minimum and maximum availability of fresh fruits and vegetables.[42]

In order to confirm or reject a medical hypothesis, the most convincing arguments come from epidemiological studies, performed on large cohorts during a sufficiently long time. The data was subject to multivariate analysis, and potential covariates are: age, sex, cigarette smoking, alcohol consumption and body weight. The associations between life style, diet and disease development can be found.

Such epidemiological studies have indicated that in most developed countries, high dietary intakes of saturated fat and cholesterol positively correlate with mortality from heart disease. **In simple words it means, more fatty bacon - more heart attacks.** However, with similar fat intakes as in the USA or UK, mortality rates in south France are significantly lower. This finding was paradoxical! Since a distinguishing feature of the French diet is the consumption of red wine with meals, the discovery has become known as the "**French paradox**" (see section 8.3). This has prompted numerous studies on the association between moderate alcohol consumption, especially of red wine, and the risk of cardiovascular diseases.

Unlike the USA or North European countries population, the French and Italian populations also have the benefits of a **Mediterranean diet** rich in antioxidants.

Over 200 studies in the epidemiological literature relate to the lack of adequate consumption of fruits and vegetables to cancer incidence and cardiovascular disease. The quarter of the population with a low dietary intake of fruits and vegetables has a double cancer rate for most types of cancer (lung, stomach, colon, bladder). European countries with low fruit and vegetable intake (e.g. Scandinavian ones) are generally in poorer health and have higher rates of cardiovascular diseases than countries with high intake (e.g., Greece, Italy).

Epidemiological studies that have been widely discussed by physicians are, for instance, the following:

•   Investigation of risk factors for chronic diseases started in 1980; over **800 elderly Dutch** men from Zutphen aged 65-84 were observed, the study was extended for 5 years in 1985-1990. The major sources of flavonoids were tea, onions and apples. Intakes of flavonoids were inversely related to the coronary heart disease mortality[43].

•   The survey covered **8,558 Japanese** residents of the town of Yoshimi over 40 years old (in 1986-1990); the inverse association between consumption of green tea and various serum biomarkers (total cholesterol, triglyceride, HDL/LDL) showed that green tea might act protectively against cardiovascular diseases and disorders of the liver[44].

•   **10,000 Finns** were observed for 20 years[45], and their high consumption of fruit and vegetables was highly correlated with lower lung cancer rate.

•   Vitamin C might be protective for several chronic diseases. Almost **20,000 English men and women** age 45-79 years old were examined. Plasma ascorbic acid concentration was inversely related to mortality from all-causes, including cardiovascular disease and ischemic heart disease. The risk of mortality in the top ascorbic acid quintile was about half the risk in the lowest quintile. The relation with mortality was continuous through the whole distribution of ascorbic acid concentrations; 20 micromole/L rise in plasma ascorbic acid concentration (equivalent to about 50 g per day increase in fruit and vegetable intake), was associated with about a 20% reduction in risk of all-cause mortality, independent of age, systolic blood pressure, blood cholesterol, cigarette smoking habit, diabetes, and supplement use.

• Epidemiologic studies have suggested that vitamin E (alpha-tocopherol) may play a preventive role in reducing the incidence of atherosclerosis. The Cambridge Heart Antioxidant Study, CHAOS[47], found a 47% reduction in fatal and nonfatal myocardial infarction in patients with proven coronary atherosclerosis who were given 400 or 800 IU of vitamin E daily. There was, however, no effect on mortality. Nevertheless, the emerging and promising data suggest the potential benefit of vitamin E for high-risk cardiac patients.

It is commonly believed that the beneficial effects of vitamin C and E increase with the consumed amounts – which is not true! Researchers have found that the U-curve exists when the risk factors of vitamins are considered.

Vitamin C is marketed as an antioxidant supplement and claimed to increase resistance to oxidative stress and diseases. However, in addition to its well-known antioxidant properties, vitamin C can also act as a pro-oxidant. The *in vitro* induction of lipid peroxidation by ascorbate/iron systems is a popular standard assay for inducing oxidative stress and testing antioxidant activity. More interesting are results showing antioxidant status *in vivo*. Intakes of vitamin C below the recommended dose are associated with increased free-radical damage to DNA, but the same is supplementation with high-dose vitamin C. The balance between beneficial and toxic effects of vitamin C supplementation was assessed in the study[48] in which 30 healthy volunteers received supplements of 500 mg of vitamin C per day for 6 weeks. The level of modified DNA bases was detected in blood lymphocytes, and the level of 8-oxoguanine decreased upon supplementation whereas the level of 8-oxoadenine increased. Both compounds represent mutagenic lesions and this observation indicates that the balance between anti- and prooxidative biochemical reactions is more complex.

Similar observations were made for vitamin E. Vitamin E supplements were protective against cardiovascular disease in the CHAOS study but an apparent rise in fatal myocardial infarction after treatment with RRR-α-tocopherol (pure, biologically active stereoisomer) was found. Fatal infarction is often associated with rupture of advanced unstable plaques and a high-dose of vitamin E could facilitate rupture by exerting pro-oxidant effects. Pro-oxidant action of vitamin E takes place when tocopherol radicals are formed in large quantities and react with lipids. In the presence of co-existing antioxidants such as vitamin C or flavonoids these radicals are reduced back to parent α-tocopherol.

Therefore, administration of high doses of vitamin E alone is not beneficial when other antioxidants are missing.

This biochemical rationale explains why foods containing small levels of vitamin E, but also co-antioxidants, provide greater health benefits than vitamin E supplements. The contradictory results of epidemiological studies clearly point at the importance of balanced antioxidant networks and the risks related to unbalanced networks when only one member is highly increased. It also confirms the conventional wisdom that the best source of nutrients and phytochemicals is diversified food, not single-component supplement.

Should we take supplements with antioxidant vitamins? Yes, but caution is required when formulating recommendations and dosages since the downward (deficit) as well as the upward slope of the U-curve should be kept in mind.

An observation, that high doses of antioxidant vitamins, especially those soluble in lipids (A and E) exert pro-oxidant action is called the "antioxidant paradox". It is worth remembering that the more vitamins A, C and E does not mean the better.

Halliwell[49 50] tried to explain the paradoxical observations that administration of antioxidants can give protective effects or worsen damage:

• human cells generally function in a reduced state but some degree of localized oxidation is needed (to permit proteins folding, several gene transcription, apoptosis)

• administration of a powerful reducing agent (antioxidant) after the oxidative damage has started could promote damage

• the association between oxidative stress and disease should not be exaggerated, i.e., in most human diseases oxidative stress is a secondary phenomenon, not the primary cause of the disease.

How do we know if we take sufficient amounts of antioxidant vitamins? The antioxidant status of body fluids is the most informative. The profile of plasma antioxidants can be measured as well as total antioxidant capacity of blood serum (plasma).

The daily dose of 60-80 mg vitamin C is sufficient to prevent scurvy, but body weight should be taken into account; simple indication holds: amount of vitamin C in mg = body weight in kg.

Recently, larger doses are recommended, ca. 180-200 mg, producing the concentration in blood plasma equal to 70 µM. Severe vitamin C deficiency (below 6-10 µM) has been known for many centuries as the potentially fatal disease - scurvy. Symptoms of scurvy include bleeding and bruising easily, hair and tooth loss, swelling and joint pain. Such symptoms appear to be related to the weakening of blood vessels, connective tissue, and bone, which contain collagen. Vitamin C is required for the synthesis of collagen, norepinephrine (neurotransmitter), carnitine (essential for the transport of fat to cellular organelles), and is involved in the metabolism of cholesterol to bile acids.

In the USA, the recommended dietary allowance for vitamin C was recently revised upward from 60 mg daily for men and women. The recommended daily allowance (RDA) continues to be based primarily on the prevention of deficiency disease, rather than the prevention of chronic disease and the promotion of optimum health. The recommended intake for smokers is 35 mg/day higher than for non-smokers, because smokers are under increased oxidative stress from the toxins in cigarette smoke, and generally have lower blood levels of vitamin C.

It is worth mentioning that vitamin E is a term used to describe a family of tocopherols (eight antioxidants, four tocopherols, alpha-, beta-, gamma- and delta-, and four tocotrienols) of which α-tocopherol is the most abundant. These compounds are located in membranes and protect membrane phospholipids for oxidation. Fats, which are an integral part of all cell membranes, are vulnerable to destruction through oxidation by free radicals. The fat-soluble vitamin, α-tocopherol, is uniquely suited to intercepting free radicals and preventing a chain reaction of lipid destruction. Aside from maintaining the integrity of cell membranes throughout the body, α-tocopherol also protects the fats in low-density lipoproteins (LDL) from oxidation. Oxidized LDLs have been implicated in the development of cardiovascular diseases.

Although the true vitamin E deficiency is rare, suboptimal intake of vitamin E is relatively common. The dietary intake and blood levels of α-tocopherol in 16,295 multi-ethnic adults in the USA were examined, and 28-41% participants were found to have blood levels of tocopherol less than 20 µM/l (below this level a risk for cardiovascular disease increased). There are suggestions to take more than the recommended

5-15 mg daily (even 500 mg). However, human intervention studies in which male smokers were exposed during 5-8 years to daily supplementation with vitamin E did not reveal any effect on the overall mortality, but did show increased mortality resulting from haemorrhage stroke.

Importantly, the latest RDA for vitamin E continues to be based on the prevention of deficiency symptoms rather than on health promotion and the prevention of chronic disease. Meydani, expressed the opinion[51], that **supplementation with vitamin E is more reasonable in prevention than in the treatment of cardiovascular disease**.

The antioxidant and radical scavenging abilities are also exhibited by carotenoids. Their antioxidant properties depend on the number of conjugated double bonds in the molecule. Beta-carotene and other carotenoids that can be converted by the body into retinol (retinol, retinal, retinoic acid, and related compounds are known as retinoids, vitamin A) are referred to as provitamin A carotenoids. Hundreds of different carotenoids are synthesized by plants, but only about 10% of them are provitamin A carotenoids.

The deficit of carotenoids in the diet has negative influences on human health[52]. The **earliest evidence of vitamin A deficiency is impaired dark adaptation or night blindness**. Vitamin A deficiency among children in developing nations is the leading (preventable) cause of blindness. Retinoic acid and its isomers affect gene expression and thereby influence numerous physiological processes. Studies in cell culture and animal models have documented the capacity for retinoids and carotenoids to reduce carcinogenesis. However, the results of human studies examining the relationship between the consumption of vitamin A and cancer are less clear. Two major trials even found increased cancer incidence after β-carotene supplementation in both smokers and asbestos workers[53]. The results of the Carotene And Retinol Efficacy Trial (CARET) suggest that high-dose supplementation of vitamin A and β-carotene should be avoided in people at high risk of lung cancer. About 9,000 people (smokers and people with asbestos exposure) were assigned a daily regimen of 25,000 IU of retinol and 30 milligrams of β-carotene. Unfortunately, after four years of follow-up the incidence of lung can-

The carotenoids include:

β-carotene and α-carotene,
β-cryptoxantin,
zeaxantin,
astaxantin,
lutein,
lycopene

Chemical formula of β-carotene

cer was 28% higher in the supplemented group[54].

Natural, plant derived polyphenols have antioxidant properties and show protective effects against cardiovascular disease or certain forms of cancer. These findings have contributed to the dramatic increase in the consumption and use of dietary supplements containing high concentration of flavonoids.

However, the relationship between the dose of flavonoid and health benefits is not linear. This is a common mistake to think that if a little of something is good than more is better.

At higher doses, flavonoids may act as pro-oxidants that generate free radicals, as mutagens, and as inhibitors of key enzymes. Therefore, in high doses, the adverse effects of flavonoids may outweigh their beneficial ones.

In the USA, the daily dietary intake of flavonoids is in the range of 500 to 1,000 mg. It can even be several grams when the diet is supplemented with flavonoid-containing herbal preparations (such as Ginkgo biloba, Pycnogenol, grape seed extract or green tea extract). The use of food supplements became "trendy"

and the health-conscious individuals consumed too much. Quercetin, a flavonol, is the dominating flavonoid in the human diet and estimates of human consumption are in the range of 4 to 68 mg/day (based on epidemiological studies in the USA, Europe and Asia). The doses recommended by manufacturers might far exceed the flavonoid dose one could attain from a typical American diet. For example, recommended dose of quercetin supplements range between 500 and 1,000 mg/day, which is 10 to 20 times what can be consumed in a vegetarian diet.[55]

In the scientific literature, as well as in the media, antioxidants stimulate keen interest - it is also called the "antioxidant paradox". The reason is obvious: antioxidants are not just involved with major diseases (heart infarct, cancer, diabetes), but conditions such as aging and resistance to diseases.

8.3

RED WINE AND "FRENCH PARADOX"

Biological effects of compounds present in red wine have been studied for years, but an explosion of interest occurred in early 1990's. Two publications, which appeared in 1992/94 in the respectable medical journal *Lancet* stated that red wine has beneficial effects because it inhibits the platelet aggregation and oxidation of low density lipoprotein[56].

Epidemiological studies performed in seven European countries indicated that high dietary intakes of saturated fat, cholesterol and total fat positively correlate with mortality from heart disease.

The finding that French saturated fat intake is similar to that of other developed countries while French mortality from heart attack is only one third of the average of such countries is paradoxical and has become known as the "French paradox".

To understand it, researchers have examined their distinguishing characteristics. The French have a high intake of saturated fat (14-15% of energy); other risk factor such as cigarette smoking or body mass index are no lower in France than in other industrialized countries. Lifestyle may have some contribution; the French population may live a less stressed life or take a rest at noon (siesta). One distinctive feature is the regular consumption of red wine with meals.

Many studies have shown a "U" shaped correlation between alcoholic beverage intake and total mortality; non-drinkers had a slightly higher risk for cardiovascular diseases than moderate drinkers (1-2 drinks per day) and heavy drinkers have a higher mortality due to hypertension, liver disorders, accidents or cancers.

Moderate consumption of red wine has shown to be beneficial in the prevention of atherosclerosis and coronary heart disease.

Oxidation of low-density lipoprotein (LDL) is recognized as the first step leading to atherosclerosis; oxidized LDL deposits at lesion sites of the arterial wall. It stimulates inflammatory reactions, causes monocytes and macrophages to accumulate and forms foam cells and atherogenic plaques. The studies conducted *in vitro*, with animal models and with humans, suggest that polyphenolic compounds of red wine can play a protective role in the development of atherosclerosis. Oxidative stress causes depletion of antioxidants (vitamin E) within several hours; antioxidants supplied with meals may react directly in the digestive tract, then in the blood serum and can regenerate vitamin E.

It seemed interesting to verify the extent of oxidative stress induced by a meal at plasma and LDL level, and to investigate the capacity of red wine to counteract this action. Six healthy men ate the same test meal consisting of "Milanese" meat and fried potatoes. The meal was taken either with 400 ml red wine or with an isocaloric hydroalcoholic solution. Oxidative stress at plasma level was estimated through the measure of ascorbic acid, alpha-tocopherol, protein SH groups, uric acid, and antioxidant capacity, measured before and 1h and 3h after the meal. The change in the resistance of LDL to oxidative modification was taken as an index of exposure to pro-oxidants. The meal taken with wine provoked a significant increase in the total plasma antioxidant capacity and in the plasma concentration of alpha-tocopherol and SH groups. Postprandial LDL was obtained after the wine meal was as resistant or more resistant to lipid peroxidation than fasting LDL.

Can red wine be replaced by red grape juice? Antioxidant effects on lipoproteins LDL of red and white wine, red grape juice and beer were compared. In the *in vitro* assays, both grape juice and wine inhibited oxidative processes (white wine and beer were weak antioxidants, ethanol did not act at all). However the **effect *in vivo* was strong only after the intake of red wine**. Grape juice and wine have similar contents of total polyphenols but in fresh juice there are more polymeric polyphenols and flavonoids, which are hardly soluble in water. Such compounds are better soluble in water-alcohol mixtures and the observed differences may be explained by the differences in the bioavailability of particular components.

A question arises: which constituents of wine are important for protection from coronary heart disease? The chemistry of wine is

Major phenolic constituents of red wine	
catechin, epicatechin, epigallocatechin	
procyanidins (dimers)	
oligomers of catechin and tannins	
anthocyanin pigments:	malvidin-3-0-glucoside
glycosides of:	kaempferol,
	quercetin,
	myricetin
phenolic acids:	caffeic,
	ferulic,
	gallic
cis and trans-resveratrol	

rather complex and not all compounds have been identified.

Anthocyanins, glucosides of malvidin, peonidin, petunidin and cyanidin are responsible for the beautiful red color of wine and known as strong antioxidants. The major antioxidant activity of the anthocyanins can be ascribed to the reducing power of the ortho-dihydroxy structure of the B-ring, as in cyanidin and catechin (see Fig. I). The mean total activity of red wine has been determined from the individual constituents and the main contributors are: catechin, epicatechin, gallic acid and malvidin-3-O-glucoside (190, 82, 95 and 24 mg/l, respectively), i.e., the most abundant compounds.

Are they present only in red grapes? No, the same compounds are also present in small dark colored

artery endothelial cells in response to tannin[59]. Similar endothelium-dependent relaxation activity is caused by the mixture of procyanidins (grape seeds extract), active compounds from grape skins or tannic acid.

It is worth reminding that procyanidins and tannins are the constituents of Aronia berries and other fruits. These constituents of the phenolic fraction of red wine were widely distributed in the plant kingdom and consumed by humans.

Resveratrol (3, 5, 4'- trihydroxystilbene) was the exception because red wine seemed to be the only elixir, which gave access to this species. It occurs in grapes but later was also found in peanuts and cranberries. Its concentration in red wine varies considerably. For instance, in wine produced with Cabernet Sauvignon grapes in Napa Valley (California, USA) the 1989 vintage contained

Summing up, it was pointed[58] for three possible explanations of the "French paradox":

1. ethanol itself has potentially beneficial effects, eliminating blood clots, plasma fibrinogen falls

2. polyphenols from wine (anthocyanins, polymeric catechins, phenolic acids) – owing to antioxidant properties may delay the progress of atherogenic processes by inhibiting the oxidation of lipids.

3. wine may affect blood vessel function because it contains compounds that relax aortic endothelium. The relaxation produced by grape products involves nitric oxide and the intracellular messenger for NO is guanylate cyclase.

fruits and berries, including Aronia. Aronia berries contain epicatechin and its oligomers and polymers (condensed tannins) as well as anthocyanins – glycosides of cyanidin.

In 1989 it was found that NO is released from rabbit pulmonary

0.09 mg/l resveratrol, whereas the 1994 vintage contained as much as 8.9 mg/l. After chronic consumption of moderate amounts of red wine containing a known concentration of resveratrol, its blood levels in healthy volunteers ranged from 100 nM to 1 µM. Are these levels sufficient to justify biological effects? At first glance, the answer would have to be no, but after careful examination of the data it leads to a different conclusion. Biological effects obtained with very low doses of resveratrol are beneficial to the cardiovascular system.

Resveratrol inhibits platelet aggregation and may protect against arteriosclerosis, it is an antioxidant with anti-inflammatory and anticancer properties.

Another interesting matter that has been widely discussed, concerns the **color of red wine**. Wine, as it is widely known, can be stored for years and achieve a very high price. Professor R. Brouillard from the Strasbourg University (France), who did a lot of work on wine antioxidant properties, told a story about the discovery of Burgundy red wine bottles. They had been hidden underneath a coal heap in a Parisian cellar a little before the German invasion in 1940 and remained there for at least four decades. Nobody was surprised that Pinot Noir wines have retained their original red color although anthocyanin dyes are unstable in aqueous medium like wine. According to Brouillard, the paradox is that the Pinot Noir vine is at the origin of the world's best red wines (and its anthocyanins are relatively simple when compared with the diversity of anthocyanidin glycosides affecting flower colors in petunia).

Simple anthocyanins are not believed to remain stable for a long time; they have to combine with tannins and/or evolve to another dyes. As it was shown in the early 1980's, during the aging of red wine, the polymeric catechins and tannins are formed[61]. The process of wine aging has become a major field of research in **oenology** and many researchers are now analyzing novel wine pigment structures. Malvidin-3-O-glucoside (oenin) is a starting compound used to produce novel pigments, it possesses a free 5-OH group in the A-ring, a key element in the formation of new compounds. Fulkrand and collaborators[62] revealed the exis-

tence of new wine pigments (Fig.10), they were called **vitisins** (further publications appeared in 1999-2003).

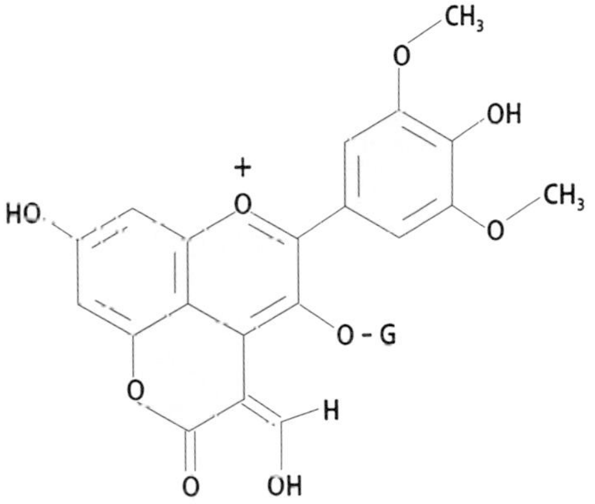

Fig. 10. Structure of vitisin, stable red pigment found in red wine

Anthocyanins from flower petals are acylated or stabilized by copigmentation. Intermolecular interactions such as hydrogen bonds or stacking of aromatic rings (sandwich configuration) keep flavylium fragment away from water and stabilize the red color of anthocyanin. In the aqueous-alcoholic solution, such as wine, flavylium cation is exposed to degradation reactions.

• Brouillard pointed out that the well-known "French paradox" has two versions. First was a discovery **that red wine has health beneficial effects. It may be called the "French paradox, step I"**.

• However, after over 10 years of intense investigations there has been no clear answer as to which of the components is responsible for the beneficial effects brought to human health. Are the fresh grape and wine species active or red wine genuine pigments discovered recently? Wine pigments vitisins, responsible for long lasting color of red wines are the next French paradox, called the "**French paradox, step II**".[63]

It is also probable that bioactive compounds, responsible for beneficial effects for health are the anthocyanins linked to (epi)catechin. Such dimers (or higher polymers with anthocyanidin unity at the end of the catechin chain) are present in red wine and Aronia extract and can explain biological activity of these two materials. Wine is a more popular beverage than Aronia or black currant juice, and therefore a majority of studies have been concentrated on the red grape antioxidants.

The interest in the wide use of red wine antioxidants for the prevention and treatment of human diseases has been called the "antioxidant paradox".

Taking into account the strong antioxidant activity of the constituents of Aronia extract, it seemed worthy to study its biological activity. It should be used in the studies of cardiovascular diseases and neurodegenerative diseases.

Preliminary clinical tests showed that Aronia extract lowers blood pressure. Especially in preventing atherogenesis, heart attack or brain infarct, the role of Aronia may be the "Polish antioxidant paradox".

Increased consumption of Aronia juice and administration of Aronia extract (supplements containing Aronia extract in capsules) can give protective effects and decrease the incidences of fatal myocardial infarction (see section 10.2).

The aging of red wine is somewhat similar to the oxidative transformation of tea, where the flavonoids from green tea leaves undergo chemical reactions. Tea, like wine is the rich source of polyphenols, which need some "maturation" treatment. Are such oxidative processes necessary to produce compounds beneficial for health?

8.4.
GREEN TEA CATECHINS

Green tea is the second well-known beverage (after red wine), and likewise intensively studied. The world owns its discovery to the Chinese.

The legends from China and India suggest that drinking tea was initiated over five thousand years ago. Drinking tea in China or Japan was associated with life style and rituals. Tea was introduced all around the world by traders and travellers and became the most popular beverage. It is popular mainly due to caffeine content and tea ingestion improves neurological and psychological functions. Traditionally, tea was drunk to improve digestion, blood flow and eliminate toxins. The past 15 years have been rich in scientific information concerning its beneficial effects on human health.

Tea contains a large amount of catechins, the compounds that could be separated and tested on the cellular level.

One cup of tea contains 50-100 mg of polyphenolic compounds characterized by strong antioxidative properties.

Their content depends on the kind of tea, technology of manufacturing of tea leaves and the preparation of infusion. The major constituents of polyphenols are illustrated in Fig. 11; epigallocatechin gallate (EGCG) is the major catechin accounting for more than 10% on a dry weight basis. All four compounds are the derivatives of (-)-epicatechin (EG).

It is interesting to note that (-)-epicatechin is also the major constituent of Aronia tannins.

It is difficult to show the benefits of drinking tea, analyzing the data from China; the poverty of the society and dramatic political and social changes make the comparisons very difficult. Japan, which enjoyed over half of a century of undisturbed development, is an example of a country with high consumption of green tea and long-lived people. The contribution of other dietary and cultural habits should also be considered; nevertheless, high consumption of green tea has positive influence.

The association between consumption of green tea and various serum markers in a Japanese population was studied [Imai, 1995], with special attention to preventive effects against cardiovascular disease and disorders of the liver. In 1986 a prospective cohort study started in the town of Yoshimi, the survey covered over 8,500 residents (95% of all

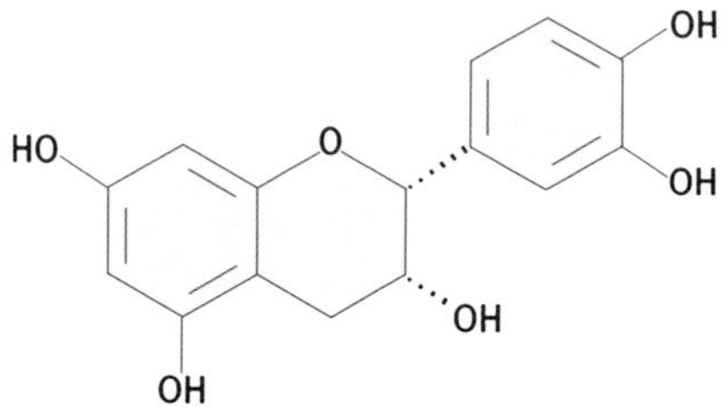

EC

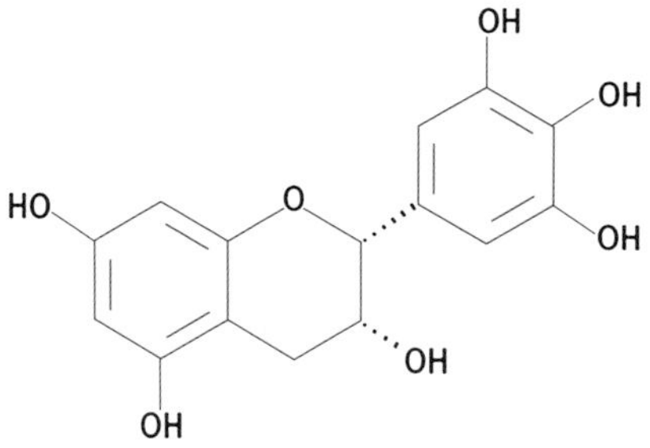

EGC

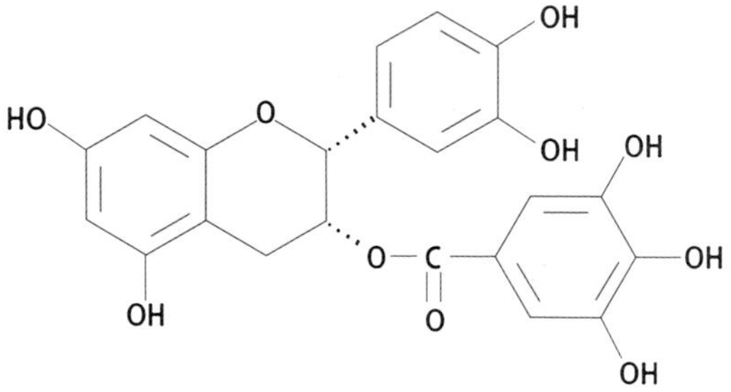

ECG

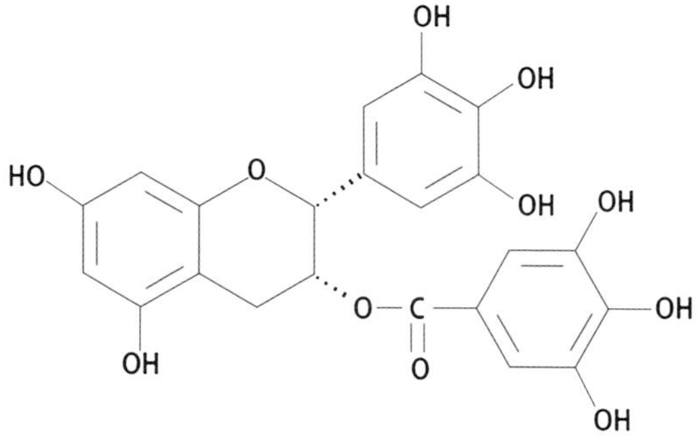

EGCG

Fig. 11. Chemical structures of tea catechins: epicatechin (EC), epigallocatechins (EGC), epicatechin gallate (ECG) and epigallocatechin gallate (EGCG).

over the age of 40). Blood samples taken in the period between 1986 and 1990 were subjected to bio-chemical and immunological assays. The results were interesting world-wide: increased consumption of green tea was associated with decreased serum concentrations of total choles-terol, triglyceride and an increased proportion of HDL to LDL (high density lipoprotein cholesterol to low and very low lipoprotein cholesterols) which resulted in a decreased athero-genic index. These results imply that green tea may act preventively against cardiovascular disease. It correlated well with observations and the preva-lence of heart disease in whole cohort. Consumption of more that 10 cups of green tea a day was relat-ed to decreased concentration of hepatological markers in serum (aspartate aminotransferase, alanine transferase, ferritin). The inverse asso-ciation of ferritin and lipid peroxides and tea consumption suggests that the tea prevents cell damage of the liver and may have protective effects on the development of cancer. The consumption of green tea was also associated with being part of a healthier surviving cohort (occasional drinkers of alcohol, non-smokers)!

The average life span of the Japanese in 2000 was 84.6 years for women and 77.6 years for men (in Poland people live 7 years less). Japan's aging population faces some difficulties such as a rising number of senile dementia or Alzheimer patients.

The third highest cause of mortality, after cancer and heart disease was cerebral stroke. One epidemiological study showed that the incidence of stroke was significantly lower in peo-ple who consume more than five cups of green tea per day.

Polyphenols of tea, especially the derivatives of epicatechin, can counteract the effects of oxidative stress and age-associated diseases.

Although green tea cannot receive official health claims (like a drug), it can be treated as a healthy drink, and a source of pharmacologi-cally active compounds. These com-pounds are effective in preventing oxidative stress induced processes in the human body.

Polyphenols of green tea act like polyphenols of Aronia berries. They support the fight against degenerative diseases such as, arteriosclerosis and cardiovascular diseases, Alzheimer's and Parkinson's disease, and cancers.

8.5.
ANTIOXIDANT FOOD SUPPLEMENTS AND FUNCTIONAL FOODS

It is now widely recognized that diet is an important determinant of human health and that it is not only avert deficiencies of micronutrients but also marginal deficiencies of sev-eral vitamins and minerals that can result in increased incidence of infections, impaired immune response and metabolic disorders.

Nevertheless, now it is clear that there is a gap between the ideal balanced diet elaborated by nutrition specialists and the reality of what people actually eat.

The best source of all nutrient needs are healthy foods. However, for those whose eating habits and food selections may not compromise nutritional adequacy (for several reasons), dietary supplements can be helpful in fulfilling the requirements. When should we take dietary supplements?

Indications for supplementation are related to age and health status:

small children *should eat diversified, healthy foods (and vitamins after consultation with a physician, pediatrician)*

adults, *especially those of high activity (endurance physical exercises, traveling a lot) may benefit from functional food, enriched in vitamins and minerals*

seniors, *besides diversified food and functional food should take supplements (for example: containing antioxidants, improving functions of brain, joints, eyes, preventing prostatitis, osteoporosis).*

Healthy adults frequently take multivitamin compositions of the "one-pill-a-day" type. Besides "dedicated" supplements, developed for athletes, pregnant women or diabetics, the supplements "for all" are those containing dietary fibers.

At present, in the typical diet of developed countries, American or European, there a is pronounced deficit of dietary fibers. The necessary fibers intake was estimated at 25-40 g per day but a typical diet covers ca. 50% of that amount. Epidemiology, clinical and laboratory studies support increased consumption of high fibers foods as part of the strategy to reduce risk of coronary heart disease, cancers of digestive tract or diabetes. Functional foods should be enriched in fibers and dedicated to obese subjects together with some slimming agents of plant origin (extracts of green tea).

Considering high mortality rates from coronary heart disease, is it worth checking whether the typical European diet covers the requirement for antioxidant vitamins and phytamins? In Poland, the staff of the Institute of Food and Nutrition analyzed food questionnaires and the content of vitamins C, A and E in the diets. A typical diet supplied 20-45% more vitamin A than the recommended dose, the intake of vitamin E reached 80-90% of daily dose. A worse situation concerns vitamin C, because the consumption of fresh sources of this vitamin is insufficient, and half of the population obtains only 40 to 60% of the necessary amounts. To prevent the deficit, especially in winter, this vitamin should be administrated as a supplement. The daily intake of flavonoids was estimated at 15-25 mg/day, similar to the intake in the Netherlands (23 mg/day/person) or in Denmark (28 mg) although new results from Finland showed much higher amounts: 65 mg/day.

According to several public health surveys, as much as 50-60% of the American adult population consumes a dietary supplement on a regular basis. Most people consume only vitamins or vitamins together with minerals. Thousands of preparations on the market meet the criteria for food supplements and advertising in the mass media encourages using them. Thus, it is important to educate people how to use supplements and when supplementation can have a beneficial effect on their health.

The intake of supplements began in the early 1980's, when the potential benefits of calcium and fish oil were supported by clinical studies and physicians began to educate consumers about these substances. Published clinical studies expanded quickly, for example: garlic to reduce atherosclerosis, cranberry juice to prevent urinary tract infections, antioxidants to reduce the risk of heart attacks. Some nutrition experts have indicated that it would be prudent for adults to consume a daily multivitamin and perhaps additional amounts of some specific nutrients, in order to ensure adequate intakes.

Health professionals, such as physicians and nurses, are also interested in rational supplementation. In 2007, the questionnaire was administered to 900 American physicians and 277 nurses (HCP Impact Study, CRN). This study revealed that 72% of physicians and 89% of nurses used dietary supplements and a large portion of them recommended supplements to their patients (79% of physicians and 82% of nurses). The reason for recommending was for overall health and wellness. The use of dietary supplements can be viewed as one of several elements of a healthy lifestyle, including control of body weight, engaging in physical activity, and not smoking.

However, it is not likely that one "super-pill" per day will replace healthy diet and supply all necessary micronutrients. The discussion continues as to the problem; should the supplementation with single vitamins be recommended or one with a combination of a few or a composition containing "almost all"?

The supplementation should meet personal needs, so the best solution would be to check the level of respective vitamins and minerals in the body fluids. Such analytical data are not standard yet but soon will be, similarly to the level of sugar in blood nowadays.

Most studies concentrated on the effects of a single vitamin or several of them. The overall effect of a comprehensive supplementation of multinutrient on the antioxidant defense system in healthy persons was studied in 2001. Young volunteers of normal life style received supplements (a full complement of multivitamins, multi-minerals and herbs) administrated in a double blind manner. Plasma vitamin C, E and β-carotene, erythrocyte vitamin E, and whole blood selenium all showed an increase after multinutrient supplementation. The activities of enzymes catalase and glutathione peroxidase increased at 16 weeks of supplementation. The delay in the increase in the activities of antioxidant enzymes is probably related to the relatively long turnover of red blood cells. For a healthy subject an elevated plasma level of small molecule antioxidant such as vitamin E would quickly result in an increase of the same in mature erythrocytes. The study showed that short-term (16 weeks) supplementation with multinutrient can beneficially modify the antioxidant system, as indicated by the improved vitamin status and elevated antioxidant enzymatic activities.

In conclusion – after 4 months of multinutrient supplementation (or its equivalent, a diet rich in fruit and vegetables), the antioxidant defense barrier (in a healthy persons) arrived the maximum.

So, one portion of capsules with vitamins and minerals taken occasionally or several meals in "Mediterranean style" are not sufficient to maintain full health.

More recent surveys have generally found that dietary supplement use in the United States represents an important source of nutrition. However, little is known about individuals who routinely consume multiple dietary supplements. In 2007, the study was undertaken to describe the dietary supplement usage patterns and health status of individuals who were daily users of multiple dietary supplements for over 20 years. Dietary supplements consumed on a daily basis by more than 50% of "multiple-supplement" users included a multivitamin /mineral, B-complex, vitamin C, vitamin E, calcium with vitamin D, a herbal immune supplement, carotenoids, omega-3 fatty acids, flavonoids, lecithin, coenzyme Q10 with resveratrol, alfalfa, and glucosamine. Among supplement users, no individuals had suboptimal serum vitamin D and C concentrations. Supplement use was also associated with lower serum triglycerides and higher HDL-cholesterol concentrations. These findings should be confirmed by studying other groups of heavy users of dietary supplements and should also be weighed in the context of potential detrimental effects of some supplements, particularly beta-carotene and alpha-tocopherol. Further research on usage patterns and the potential health effects of dietary supplements is needed.

Dieticians and other health professionals soon expect a nutritional revolution. Why? Foods have a medical value and nutraceutics urgently need clinical studies. The results may change food industry. Food companies want to make health claims for food products because they increase sales. However, **at present, a vast amount of money is allocated to promotion instead of research and development**. It is obvious that the food industry has to be research-oriented, like the pharmaceutical industry. In the USA, the food industry spends less than 0.5% of gross sales on R&D, whereas the pharmaceutical industry spends over 10%.

A majority of nutraceutical products does not have health claims and needs basic (*in vitro*) and clinical research. The results of these studies have to be presented at the scientific forum and communicated to physicians and consumers. The products like sugar and fat substitutes, fiber-enriched foods, vegetables, skim milk, low-calorie and low-carbohydrate foods, antioxidant-rich foods and so on, will be popularized and consumed for health and medical reasons.

The National Cancer Institute and the National Research Council in the USA have recommended for years the increased consumption of fruit and vegetables. In spite of the wide education efforts and the promotion of "5D" at schools and churches, only 9-17% Americans eat 5 servings of fruit and vegetables per day[67]. Dietary habits are difficult to change and result more from national or family traditions than from the actual medical indications.

Information on the antioxidant capacity of fruits and vegetables could influence individual decisions on consumption, taken at a fruit stand in the nearest supermarket.

For instance, in the case of infection or problems with memory it would be beneficial to consume more berries than bananas. It has been estimated that the daily dose of antioxidants in a typical USA diet should be 1.2-1.7 mmol of TE (Trolox equivalents, in ORAC scale). Consumption of 1/2 cup of bilberries or blueberries gives 1-3.2 mmol TE - a remarkable contribution to the antioxidant barrier of organism.

PHYSICOCHEMICAL STUDIES OF ANTIOXIDANTS

9.1.
LOOKING FOR A "SUPER-ANTIOXIDANT"

Antioxidant ingredients in beverages, fruits and vegetables have been identified and their activity compared by different assays. Which compounds have the highest activity? What are the determinants of the radical scavenging activity? There is a great interest in the question whether the antioxidant activity can be predicted on the basis of chemical properties. Generally, the number of hydroxyl groups and their position are fundamental to the antioxidant and radical scavenging activity of polyphenols, and antioxidant activity increases with the number of OH groups. Polyphenols are multifunctional and can react as simple reducing agents, oxygen radical quenchers and hydrogen donating antioxidants.

The antioxidant hierarchy based on the reduction potentials E (V) was determined by an electrochemical technique cyclic voltammetry[68]. The studied phenolic antioxidants behaved similarly, oxidation gives rise to the short-living (less than one second) products, phenoxyl radicals, which are easily reduced. The steady state radical concentration generated during electrochemical oxidation was found to be low and without the use of a special "spin trap" any EPR signal was recorded, even when the samples were frozen immediately in liquid nitrogen. Reduction potentials for the flavonoid phenoxyl radicals may predict their regeneration, although the dimerisation or polymerisation reactions may yield products from which the parent phenol cannot be obtained. **The reduction potentials of flavonoid radicals are lower than those of alkyl peroxyl radicals and the superoxide radical, which means that flavonoids may inactivate these species and prevent the consequences of their reactions.**

The spectrophotometric technique was widely applied to characterize the antioxidant activity of flavonoids. The TEAC (Trolox equivalent antioxidant activity) assay measures the concentration of Trolox (a water soluble vitamin E analogue) solution (in mM) with an equivalent antioxidant potential to a standard concentration (1 mM) of the compound under investigation. The TEAC reflects the ability of the hydrogen donating antioxidants to scavenge the ABTS$^{\bullet+}$ radical cation, compared with that of Trolox.[69]

Table 4.

Antioxidant properties of some flavonoids: electrochemical reduction potentials E (V) and the values of TEAC (Trolox Equivalent Antioxidant Capacity)

Flavonoid	Number of OH groups	Reduction potentials E (V)	TEAC (mM)
Chrysin	2	0.83	1.43
Naringenin	3	0.76	1.53
Kaempferol	4	0.39	1.34
Catechin	5	0.36	2.40
Epicatechin	5	0.33	2.50
Morin	5	0.34	2.55
Quercetin	5	0.29	4.70
Myricetin	6	0.20	3.10

Chemical compounds bearing numerous OH groups (like myricetin) and having a low reduction potential exhibit high values of TEAC and are strong antioxidants. The relationship is not linear; for example, quercetin with five OH groups has a higher value of TEAC than myricetin with six OH groups. It seems obvious that structurally related polyphenolic compounds should react with a radical according to a similar mechanism. However, OH groups substituted at para or meta positions to aromatic ring may have different reactivity. Additionally, the OH group involved in intramolecular hydrogen bond (e.g. C5-OH...O=C) is less reactive towards radicals.

It is not possible to construct a linear relationship between one parameter, which characterizes the structure (e.g., the number of OH groups) and the antioxidant activity for several hundreds of polyphenolic compounds.

However, the mechanism of action and the reactivity should be determined for every particular compound as well as for their mixtures. Flavonoids are excellent antioxidants, and for the human diet their antioxidant capacity are comparable to or even superior to that of vitamin C and E.

It is generally accepted that polyphenolic antioxidants Ar-OH may react with peroxyl radicals:

ROO$^{\bullet}$+ArOH→ROOH+ArO$^{\bullet}$

The radicals have very short lifetimes and recombine:

ArO$^{\bullet}$+R OO$^{\bullet}$→ROO-Ar=O

Stable products of such reactions are corresponding quinones (ortho-quinones). In the studies of antioxidant activity several radical species can be used:

- synthetic free radicals as ABTS• (2,2'-azinobis-3-ethylbenzo-thiazoline-6-sulfonic acid, TEAC assay) and DPPH• (2,2-diphenyl-1-picrylhydrazyl, DPPH assay),

- physiologically relevant peroxyl radicals (generated in ORAC assay)

- Fe^{+3}/Fe^{+2} ions (ferric to ferrous reducing ability, FRAP assay).

A comparison of H-donating antioxidant activities is commonly made by three assays: TEAC, ORAC and FRAP. Usually, compounds characterized as strong antioxidants are effective scavengers of all free radicals, but there is no straight-line correlation between the data obtained from, for instance, TEAC and DPPH-assay. One reason may be an electric charge at a radical (e.g. $ABTS^{•+}$) and at an antioxidant molecule (e.g. flavylium cation of anthocyanidins).

The hierarchy of antioxidant activities of the fruits and vegetables showed that fruits that are rich in anthocyanins have a higher antioxidant potential than those rich in flavanones, flavanols or hydroxycinnamic acids. It is in agreement with the hierarchy of antioxidant potential estimated for the diverse types of phenolic compounds in all *in vitro* assays. The anthocyanins generally have shown higher antioxidant activity than other phenolic compounds.

Taking into account the results of *in vitro* **assays – anthocyanins are "super-antioxidants" and the enormous antioxidant potential of berries results mainly from high anthocyanin content.**

However, the antioxidant activity can be significantly modified in non-polar surrounding, such as lipids.

The antioxidant activity of the six common anthocyanidins, pelargonidin, cyanidin, delphinidin, peonidin, petunidin, and malvidin, and their glycosidic forms was evaluated[70] in lipid-containing models (human low-density lipoprotein (LDL) and emulsified methyl linoleate). In addition, the radical scavenging activity of the compounds against the DPPH• radical was studied. In bulk methyl linoleate, anthocyanins and anthocyanidins possessed only a weak antioxidant activity or even oxidation-promoting activity. Depending on the anthocyanidin, different glycosylation patterns either enhanced or diminished the antioxidant power. For the most part, the activities of the glycosides and the aglycones did not differ remarkably in emulsion. In LDL the aglycones showed in general higher activities than the glycosides. In bulk oil, to the contrary, the glycosides were more effective than the aglycones. **However, most anthocyanins and their aglycones acted as strong antioxidants in emulsion and LDL**. These compounds showed an activity comparable to the well-known antioxidants quercetin and catechin, which possess the structural features determining radical scavenging ability: hydroxyl groups in the B ring (preferably ortho-hydroxy, as in cyanidin) and the 3,5-OH groups in the A and C rings.

9.2.
ELECTRON PARAMAGNETIC RESONANCE (EPR) IN THE STUDIES OF ANTIOXIDANTS

The most sensitive method of free radicals detection is the spectroscopy of electron paramagnetic resonance (EPR). EPR spectrum of a radical can be registered even at concentrations of 10-12M. A more important limitation is the short lifetime. Majority of radicals live only a fraction of a second and cannot be registered without specially constructed equipment (a flow technique) and/or low temperature (freezing in liquid nitrogen or helium).

Antioxidant, radical scavenging properties can be tested using stable radicals, such as nitroxide radicals, galvinoxyl radical or 1,1-diphenyl-2-picrylhydrazyl radical (DPPH·).

The idea is relatively simple: first EPR spectrum of standard solution of a radical is registered (Fig. 12), its

intensity is assumed as 100%. Next, a droplet (10-50 ìl) of solution with an antioxidant (or mixture of antioxidants) is added and the decay of radical signal is followed in time. The concentration of radical, e.g. DPPH· decreases according to the reaction (where Ar-OH depicts a phenolic antioxidant):

DPPH·+Ar-OH→DPPH-H+Ar-O·

Radical Ar-O· is a short-living species and undergoes immediate recombination; usually it is not registered in the EPR spectrum at room temperature.

The results, expressed in % (Z%) can be taken as a measure of antioxidant properties of a particular single compound since the decrease in

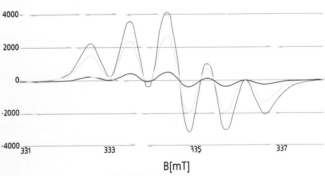

Fig. 12. EPR spectra of the DPPH radical: standard solution (black contour), after adding the extract of black grapes (green contour), after adding the same amount of anthocyanins of Aronia (bordeaux contour).

DPPH⋅ signal is a linear function of the concentration of the antioxidant.

In 1989, the Japanese applied the DPPH assay to the studies of antioxidant properties of tannins.[71] In the Department of Physical Chemistry, Faculty of Pharmacy, Medical University of Warsaw, Poland, the method has been adapted in order to test various materials, such as pharmaceutical preparations, foods or dietary supplements. The results for fruit and herbal teas, fruit juices, syrups and wines are included in Table 5, for comparison.

The concentration of the stock solution of DPPH was not the same for wine as for syrup. However, these products can be compared to each other since the whole series was tested in the same conditions. For example, fruit teas in bags were poured with hot water and allowed to soak for 5 minutes. The test solution was close to that usually consumed.

At the top of the list one can find fruit teas containing rosehips as a major ingredient. These fruits are known as a rich source of vitamin C (the "Condition" tea contains a vitamin-mix) and therefore they exhibit strong radical scavenging properties. In other teas, the dark colored fruit or berries are the dominating ingredients; they are responsible for strong antioxidant properties due to high content of anthocyanins, catechins and phenolic acids.

Products containing Aronia are located at the top places in all categories. Aronia juice is the strongest antioxidant among all fruit juices; likewise, Aronia syrup is the strongest antioxidant among syrups.

Somewhat surprising results have been obtained for the studied fruit wines. The beverages prepared by fermentation of small dark fruits, such as cherry, black currant or Aronia exhibited strong antioxidant properties, comparable to that of red grape wine. This finding is paradoxical. In our laboratory, we tested several homemade fruit wines, prepared according to the old recipes.

It looks like our grandparents were able to manufacture at home, from local fruits and berries, alcoholic beverages with excellent radical scavenging properties!

The very high content of total polyphenols, the high content of anthocyanins and strong radical scavenging properties are the features of fruit wines produced in Poland by professional manufacturers. These wines have been subjected to analyses using modern NMR, EPR and HPLC techniques. The studies performed at the Medical University of Warsaw showed that the wines contain the whole profile of valuable bioactive compounds. Undoubtedly, the wine produced from Aronia should exhibit health beneficial properties and can be recommended as a sound part of a diet. It cannot be granted official health claims since there are no clinical studies of this product.

Yet underestimated, Aronia wine or Aronia tinctures are promising, relatively cheap alcoholic beverages which can offer protection to the cardiovascular system. Moderate consumption of Aronia wine could contribute to the "Polish paradox", i.e., lowering the risks of heart attacks in citizens, consuming a lot of saturated fat with traditional Polish meals.

The same is true for European and American citizens also enjoying pommes frits with fried meat and a very small leaf (if any) of lettuce.

Dietary supplements in capsules or tablets contribute to a positive life style and good health, and their regular use can be a cost-effective strategy for promoting health. As the population of industrialized countries continues to grow older, the desire to improve life quality and lower the risk of degenerative diseases becomes even stronger. A large body of scientific evidence showed clear health benefits of certain supplements such as calcium and vitamin D for bone health. The relationship between antioxidant vitamins and nutrients and purported health benefits still needs more investigations, although the role of oxidative stress as an underlying factor in disease is well established. More and more evidence indicates that a proper balance between oxidants and antioxidants is involved in maintaining health and longevity. Therefore, antioxidant substances such as vitamins E, A and C, flavonoids, carotenoids, lipoic acid and other are the major constituents of dietary supplements. Popular preparations contain flavonoid-rich botanical extracts: green tea, grape skins and seeds, garlic, Ginkgo-biloba, Panax ginseng.

Are some supplements with antioxidants better than other?

It is always recommended to consult a physician or pharmacist as to the expected health benefits and side effects of a particular supplement and not to rely on the mass-media information. Herbal preparations can vary widely in total content of active components due to the conditions of growing, harvesting, storage and processing methods of plant materials. They should be standardized, i.e., contain standard levels of particular bioactive compounds. Their antioxidant properties could be checked by suitable assays (ORAC, FRAP, TEAC) or by reaction with stable radical DPPH.

The test of radical scavenging properties of some supplements was performed at Medical University of Warsaw using EPR spectroscopy. The preparations were purchased from a drugstore, and the results of the assay - the antioxidant capacities are illustrated in Fig. 13. The antioxidant capacity (Z%) was calculated per 1 capsule because the amounts of

Table 5.

A comparison of DPPH• radical scavenging properties for a series of products containing natural polyphenolic antioxidants.

Products	Z%
Fruit and herbal teas [ref. Acta Polon. Pharm, 58 (2001) 283]	
1."Rose" hips (contains: rose hips, elderberry)	88.0
2."Condition" (rose hips, hawthorn, vitamin mix)	75.0
3."Black currant" (black currant, elderberry)	65.0
4."Spring tea" (rose hips, Aronia, elderberry, hibiscus)	61.0
5."Aronia" (Aronia, rose hips, hawthorn)	59.0
6."Forest tea" (bilberry, raspberry, Aronia)	56.0
7."Hawthorn tea" (hawthorn fruit, raspberry)	32.0
Fruit juices and nectars [ref. Zwienie czlowieka i metabolizm, 28, (2001) 99]	
1. Aronia juice	74.4
2. Aronia nectar	71.4
3. black currant juice	57.0
4. sour cherry juice	31.5
5. orange juice	28.3
6. red grape juice	18.8
7. white grape juice	1.4
Fruit syrups [ref. Farmacja Polska, 53 (2002) 971]	
1. Aronia syrup	70.0
2. black currant syrup	68.0
3. sour cherry syrup	65.0
4. rose hips syrup	51.0
5. raspberry syrup	45.0
6. citric syrup	31.0
7. orange syrup	30.0
Wine [ref. Lek w Polsce, 7, (2001) 4]	
1. red grape wine, Bulgarian, from Melnik	74.3
2. cherry wine, Polish, product of Vinkon S.A.	66.0
3. red grape wine, French, type Pinot Noir	62.2
4. wine from Aronia, semi-dry (Vinkon)	54.0
5. wine from Aronia, sweet (Vinkon)	42.0
6. wine from black currant (Vinkon)	13.0
7. white grape wine, French	12.0
8. white grape wine, Bulgarian	8.4

active antioxidants were difficult to establish quantitatively. The extract of Aronia berries (Aronox) exhibited the strongest radical scavenging properties, followed by the red grape extract (Antiox). Medisoya (the last one in the hierarchy), is not an antioxidant product; this supplement was developed for women to mitigate menopausal disorders. Soya is rich in isoflavonoids, phytoestrogens but weak antioxidants. Extract from Ginkgo biloba is likewise not proposed as supplement with antioxidants, although it is rich in flavonoids (gingko-flavone glycosides) and exhibits radical scavenging properties. Supplementation with Ginkgo may improve brain function.

The best biomarker, confirming the activity of antioxidant supplement in vivo would be an increase in the antioxidant capacity of blood serum, urine or saliva; such data for the studied series of supplements are not available.

9.3.
BANANAS OR BERRIES? ANTIOXIDANT PROPERTIES OF FRUITS

When buying fruit for dessert, we take into account the price and quality or preferences of our family. Sometimes it is also worth considering the knowledge on chemical composition and antioxidant properties of the fruits and berries. There are fruits characterized by particular high content of polyphenols and strong antioxidant properties, contributing significantly to the antioxidant defense barrier.

A number of studies have shown that the antioxidant capacity of fruits is correlated with the content of polyphenolic compounds. Usually, the correlation coefficients are not high because in the extract of fruits other types of compounds are present, contributing to the antioxidant capacity

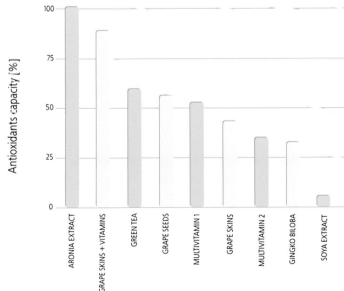

Fig. 13. The antioxidant capacity of some food supplements (per 1 capsule)

| Fruits | Polyphenols (mg /100 g) | | | ORAC[b] | FRAP[c] | TEAC[d] |
	fresh	extract[a]	dry			
Aronia	2080-2556	4010-4210	8490	160.2		
Bilberry	521	2970-3820		62.5	51.5-74.1	20.2-50
Black currants	560-799	2030-2790	3097	44.9-92.0	61.5-149.9	24.6-39.1
Red currants	210	1260-1400	1613		44.9	11.8-14.0
Raspberries		2390-2730		13.1-45.2	19.9-69.4	16.8
Sour cherries	460		3377		8.10	2.7
Red grapes				7.4	11.1	3.8-7.4
Strawberries (Senga)	225 -460	1480-1600		15.4	22.7	10.9-15.4
Cranberries	227-315	2120-2200		18.5		
Apples	205-250	1200-1300	1710	2.18	3.2	1.3-2.2
Banana				2.2	2.3	0.6-2.2
Orange	140			7.50	20.5	7.5-8.7

[a] standard gallic acid, extraction with 70% acetone.
[b] ORAC: µmole of Trolox/g fresh fruits, [c] FRAP: µmol Fe /1g of fruits, [d] TEAC: µmol Trolox/1g of fruits.

Table 6. Antioxidant potentials of fruits (according to ref.[72 73 74 75 76 77])

(e.g. vitamin C, carotenoids or tannins insoluble in water).

Investigations on antioxidant properties of fruits were performed at Linus Pauling Institute in Oregon, USA (known worldwide because of the studies on vitamin C), J. Mayer Human Nutrition Research Center on Aging at Tufts University in Boston, USA, at the University of California. In Europe, the studies from University of Helsinki, Finland and the Royal Veterinary and Agriculture University of Copenhagen, Denmark attempted to measure the antioxidant capacities of fruits, including berries, and vegetables in relation to the phenolic content.

To assess comparatively the antioxidant capacities of polyphenol-rich extracts of fruits ORAC (oxygen radical absorbance capacity, in micro molar Trolox equivalents/100g fresh weight) and FRAP (ferric reducing ability of plasma, in micro molar Fe^{+2} /100g of fresh fruit) assays were utilized.

The total antioxidant capacity, measured as ORAC, ranged from 19-131 (µM TE/g) in the extracts of the different *Vaccinium* berries, 13-146 in raspberries (*Rubus*) and 17-116 in black currants (*Ribes* genotypes) [Moyer, 2002]. Reasonable correlation between ORAC and FRAP for all 108 samples (r=0.84) suggests that either of these two measurements have validity for determining antioxidant activity with these fruits. The mechanisms of these two assays are distinct: the ability to trap a peroxyl radical with ORAC vs. ferric ion reduction with FRAP.

Different cultivars of *Vaccinium* species: *V. corymbosum, V. ashei, V. angustifolium* and *V. myrtillus* were analyzed for total polyphenolics, total anthocyanins and antioxidant capacity, ORAC. Total phenolics content ranged from 233 to 525 mg/100g, and anthocyanin concentrations in the range of 62 mg/100g for blueberries to 300 mg/100g for bilberries were observed.

When considering the antioxidant potential of fruits, people immediately ask about vitamin C. It is important to evaluate the vitamin C content because ascorbic acid is an effective radical scavenger. Obviously, the tested fruit extracts contain variable amounts of ascorbic acid. Major contributors to the antioxidant capacities of berries are anthocyanins and catechins. The content of vitamin C in berries reached 16.4 mg/100 g. The ORAC value of ascorbic acid amounts 5.6 µM TE/g, and considering its concentration it is apparent that vitamin C contribution in the total antioxidant capacity is less than 5%.

The popular statement: "fruit should be consumed because of the vitamin C content" is not valid for berries. Berries should be consumed because of their high polyphenols (anthocyanins, hydroxycinnamic acids) content, in spite of the relatively low vitamin C level.

The correlation between total anthocyanins and measurements of antioxidant capacity ORAC for various berries was not satisfying (correlation coefficient $r=0.77$), better correlation with $r=0.85$ was obtained between total phenolics and ORAC values.

Antioxidant activities ORAC for *Vaccinium* berries [Prior, 1998] and for Aronia berries [Zheng, 2003] are plotted *versus* total phenolics content in Fig. 14, and versus total anthocyanin content in Fig. 15. The surprisingly high ORAC value for Aronia berries marked with red spots corresponds with high content of polyphenolics and anthocyanins.

The profile of polyphenolic compounds of blueberry (Vaccinium corymbosum), cranberry, lingonberry and wild chokeberry was determined by chromatography (HPLC), together with their antioxidant activity. The phenolic constituents and contents among different berries varied considerably. Anthocyanins were found to be the main components in all these berries. Chlorogenic acid dominates in blueberries (616 µg/g); peonidin 3-O-galactoside in cranberries (it comprised 20.8% of the total ORAC value of 26.9 µmol TE/g) and cyanidin galactoside and arabinoside dominate in Aronia.

The characteristic feature of Aronia berries is also the high content of hydroxycinnamic acids: caffeic and chlorogenic acids contribute significantly to the antioxidant potential. The antioxidant activities of these acids are associated to some extent with the number of hydroxyl groups in their

The highest ever obtained antioxidant capacity ORAC for fruits or berries is 160 μmol TE/g for chokeberry (Aronia)!

However, these *in vitro* measurements of antioxidant capacities may or may not reflect what happens *in vivo*. Little is known about absorption

molecular structure. The antioxidant activity value for caffeic acid (two OH groups at aromatic ring) is 13.9 μmol TE/g, p-coumaric acid (one OH group) 8.6 μmol TE/g. Chlorogenic acid showed lower antioxidant activity (7.4 μmol TE/g) comparing to that of caffeic acid.

and metabolism of polyphenolic compounds.

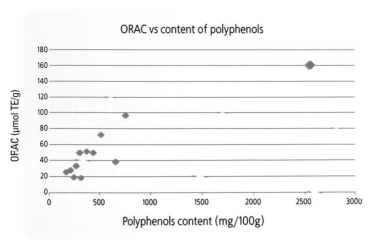

Fig. 14.

The antioxidant capacity ORAC for berries (Vaccinium) genotype [Prior, 1998] and for Aronia [Zheng, 2003] as a function of the total polyphenols content

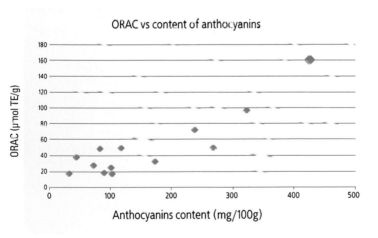

Fig. 15.

The antioxidant capacity ORAC for berries (Vaccinium) [Prior, 1998] and for Aronia [Zheng, 2003] as a function of the anthocyanins content

BIOCHEMISTRY AND MEDICINE BIOLOGICAL STUDIES OF ARONIA COMPOUNDS

Chemical compounds present in Aronia berries, polyphenols: anthocyanins, catechins, tannins and phenolic acids, have been widely studied. Physicochemical studies concentrate on their bioactive conformations, intermolecular interactions and antioxidant properties. Biochemical reactions and activities could be characterized using cell cultures and tissues, laboratory animals or healthy volunteers. The most convinced are the results of epidemiological studies on protective effects of cardiovascular diseases, cancers and other degenerative diseases of aging.

• **Protection against atherosclerosis.** As is widely known, cardiovascular diseases are the main reason of mortality and the intake of flavonoids in the diet may have protective role. The protective effect is partially explained by the inhibition of LDL oxidation and by reduced platelet aggregability. Polyphenols can be useful in the protection and restoration of endothelial function, some flavonols and also catechins and tannins produce relaxant effect of contraction of

aortic strips and reduce blood pressure. Aronia berries or Aronia extract should be included in the diet to inhibit atherosclerosis and thus to prevent heart attack and stroke.

• **Protection against cancerogenesis.** Polyphenols of Aronia can play an important role in prevention and control of cancer development since antioxidants modulate all three stages: initiation, promotion and progression of cancers. Experiments performed on mice and rats showed that the groups receiving polyphenols developed less cancer lesions in spite of a cancerogenic diet. The compounds present in Aronia berries may act as detoxifying agents by reducing oxidizing toxic substances.

• **Protection against neurodegenerative diseases.** The aging process and neurodegeneration are increasingly associated with oxidative stress. Oxidative stress contributes to Alzheimer's and Parkinson's disease, cerebral ischemia/reperfusion injuries or neuroinflammation. Oxidative stress-related neuronal decline can be inhibited by dietary intervention, supplementation of neuroprotective flavonoids. Extracts of blueberries and green tea were effective in the increasing of cognitive function, improving memory and learning.

• **Protection against UV irradiation.** More and more people decide for a sunny week (or even a weekend) flying to hot countries directly from their offices, without any accommodation period. Sunbating on the beach or strong UV in the high mountains make the sensitive skin turn red. Topically applied flavonoids prevent photooxidative stress in the skin. Ingestion of polyphenols protects against UVB-induced erythema and inflammation response. Oral supplementation of the procyanidin-rich extract increased nearly twice the mean minimal dose causing erythema (the pink color). Drinking Aronia juice or intake of Aronia extract several days before the trip, as well as using a sun-protecting cream with antioxidants allows for enjoying sunny weather longer without a harm to skin.

• **Eye diseases prevention.** Oxidative stress is implicated in the initiation of maturity onset of cataract and in the development of age-related macular degeneration. Diets rich in antioxidants may help to slow these pathological processes. Anthocyanin extracts reduce capillary permeability and fragility and may improve symptoms associated with weak eyesight (fatigue, poor night vision). A diet rich in berries or supplementation with extracts was recommended for pilots or professional drivers. At present, more and more people work watching monitors or spend several hours at a computer desk. A significant part of modern society are interested in maintaining visual acuity and may benefit from the Aronia's polyphenolics intake.

10.1.
BIOAVAILABILITY OF ANTHOCYANINS

The beneficial effect of red wine consumption against the development of atherosclerosis was attributed to the antioxidant activity of polyphenols, mainly anthocyanins. Besides anthocyanin pigments, red wine contains the flavonols, quercetin and myricetin (10-20mg/l), the flavanols catechin and epigallocatechin (up to 270 mg/l), gallic acid (95 mg/l), resveratrol (1.5 mg/l) and large amounts of condensed tannins (catechin and epicatechin polymers, 2,500 mg/l). The complex combination of various types of polyphenols makes it difficult to find out a type with the highest biological activity. The studies *in vitro* showed that the anthocyanin fraction of red wine is the most effective against hydroxyl and peroxyl radicals and inhibition of LDL oxidation, compared with phenolic acids or catechins fraction. The high efficiency of the anthocyanin fraction can be explained by its high content and by the high antioxidant potential of particular anthocyanidins.

However, are the antho-cyanins absorbed and present in body fluids? The absorption and metabolism of individual polyphenolic compounds have been studied in animals and humans, demonstrating the absorption and elimination of low micromolar amounts of their conjugates (glucuronides, sulphates, O-methyl derivatives); only a small proportion of ingested compounds is absorbed with an intact molecular structure. Bioavailability is restricted not only by limited absorption and extensive metabolism but also by such factors as degradation by the intestinal bacteria and enzymes and limited stability at various pH. Progress in analytical techniques enabled the detection of chemical compounds even at nanomol (10^{-9}M) level, and anthocyanins and their conjugates can be identified in body fluids.

It was assumed that dietary flavonoids, consumed as glycosides, are absorbed as aglycones, i.e., after prior hydrolysis of the glycosides along the digestive tract. It was thought that the glycosides are too polar to pass through the lipid membranes. Another reasonable hypothesis suggests that glucosides were absorbed intact *via* the sodium dependent glucose transporter.

In 1991 the pharmacokinetics of anthocyanosides obtained from

Vaccinium myrtillus were investigated in rats[79]. After a single oral administration, the plasma concentrations reach peak levels after 15 minutes and then rapidly decline within 2 hours. The extent of cumulative urinary and biliary elimination together with the gastrointestinal recovery demonstrated an absorption of about 5%. The low absolute bioavailability (1.2% of the administered dose) and the plasmatic peak levels of 2-3 micrograms/ml indicate modest gastrointestinal absorption.

The potential antioxidant properties of blueberry polyphenolics *in vitro* and *in vivo* have been investigated[80] using red blood cell resistance to reactive oxygen species (ROS) as the model. *In vitro* incubation with anthocyanins or hydroxycinnamic acids was found to enhance significantly blood cell resistance to ROS. This protection was also observed *in vivo*, following oral supplementation to rats at 100 mg/ml. Anthocyanins were found to afford protection at a significant level, at 6 and 24 h post supplementation. This protection presents a positive role following dietary consumption of polyphenolics from blueberries, against the formation of radicals within red blood cells *in vivo*.

In order to prove that humans absorb anthocyanins, six healthy volunteers were asked to drink 300 ml of red wine (containing 218 mg anthocyanins).[81] They were not allowed to consume any fruit nor vegetables and wine remained the only source of dietary antioxidants. Their urine showed no UV-vis absorption at 520 nm. However, after acidifying to pH=1.0 the red color appeared and disappeared at pH=5.0. Such changes are characteristic of anthocyanins, which are red at low pH due to flavylium cation and colorless at higher pH. It indicated that anthocyanins and their derivatives have been absorbed, distributed in human body and excreted.

The effect of oral supplementation with the anthocyanin-rich extract on concentration of particular anthocyanins in plasma was investigated in 2000[82]. The elderberry extract was selected due to its high concentration of anthocyanosides. Six healthy volunteers were administered spray-dried elderberry juice in gelatinous capsules containing 200 mg of dry matter with 9% of anthocyanosides. The analysis of anthocyanins in plasma is critical because their concentration is very low, however two main anthocyanins (cyanidin-3-O-glucoside and cyanidin-3-O-sambubioside) can be found using HPLC method.

Bioavailability of elderberry anthocyanins was studied in 2002 at the Tufts University, USA[83]. Four healthy women (age 67±4 years) were asked not to take supplemental vitamin in a 4-week period prior to the study and no smoking. Each of them was given **12 g of elderberry extract** in 500 ml water, the drink contained 720 mg

anthocyanins. Blood and urine samples were analyzed by HPLC and LC/MS to detect anthocyanins. The maximum plasma concentration of total anthocyanins varied from 55 to 168 nmol/l after ca. 1h. The total amount of the anthocyanins excreted during 24h was calculated to be approximately 400 μg during the first 4h. Mass spectra (molecular ions) confirmed the presence of anthocyanins in their unchanged forms in blood.

The metabolites identified as glucuronide conjugates, as well as methylated and oxidized derivatives of cyanidin 3-galactoside and cyanidin glucuronide were identified in the urine and serum after consumption of anthocyanin-rich extracts. Conjugation probably affects the biological activity of anthocyanins and these metabolic products are likely in part responsible for the reported health benefits associated with the consumption of anthocyanins.

The metabolic conversion of cyanidin glycosides in human subjects has been studied[84] using chromatography (HPLC, GC), mass spectrometry (MS), and enzymic techniques. Volunteers consumed approximately **20 g (!) chokeberry extract** containing 1.3 g cyanidin 3-glycosides (899 mg cyanidin 3-galactoside, 321 mg cyanidin 3-arabinoside, 51 mg cyanidin 3-xyloside and 50 mg cyanidin 3-glucoside). Blood samples and urine samples were collected post-consumption of the extract.

The study confirmed that: **humans have the capacity to absorb and metabolize cyanidin 3-glycosides, because at least ten individual anthocyanin metabolites were observed in the urine and serum.**

Average concentrations of anthocyanins and anthocyanin metabolites in the urine persisted in 24h urine samples at levels of 12.1 (range 11.1-13.0) nmol/l. In addition, average total levels of metabolites detected in the serum were observed at the range 197.3-986.1 nmol/l within 2h post-consumption. Cyanidin 3-galactoside accounted for 55.4% and 66.0% of the detected anthocyanins in the urine and serum samples, respectively.

Pharmacokinetic parameters and the bioavailability of several dietary anthocyanins following consumption of black currant juice and elderberry extract were compared in six healthy volunteers[85]. They were given a single oral dose of either 137 ml of black-currant juice (144.8 mg total anthocyanins) or 30 ml of elderberry extract (147.3 mg total anthocyanins). Within 7 hours, the urinary excretion of total anthocyanins was 0.04% and 0.37% of the administered dose following black currant juice and elderberry extract ingestion, respectively. The anthocyanin absorption was significantly greater following the intake of the elderberry extract than after the intake of the black currant juice.

However, in order to evaluate the contribution of anthocyanins to the health-protecting effects of the black-currant and elderberry it will be necessary to perform further studies on the particular anthocyanidins, anthocyanins and their *in vivo* metabolites in human plasma and urine.

Absorption and metabolism of delphinidin-3-O-glucopyranoside (Dp-3-glu) was studied in 2004,[86] and the metabolic pathway of cyanidin 3-O-glucopyranoside (Cy-3-glu) in 2005[87]; the studies were carried out on rats. Dp-3-glu is an anthocyanidin bearing three OH groups in B-ring and exhibits strong antioxidant properties. It appeared in blood plasma in 15 minutes after intake (100 mg/kg body weight) and the level of ca. 30 nmol/l was determined for 4h. Besides the intact Dp-3-glu also the metabolite with 4'-methoxy group was identified. Methylation of 4'-OH group at the B ring seemed to be a frequently met metabolic pathway for compounds pyrogallol-like, i.e., with three OH groups.

Cy-3-glu and its four major metabolites were detected in the blood plasma of rats after oral administration of 100 mg/kg of body mass. The plasma concentration of Cy-3-glu reached its maximum at 15 min after the ingestion. Metabolites showed their maximum plasma levels at 15, 30, 60 and 120 min. The maximum plasma concentrations of the four metabolites were in the range 5-21 nM. When Cy-3-glu was directly njected into the neck vein, only two metabolites were detected in the plasma, indicating that other two were produced during absorption from the gastrointestinal tract. Tandem mass spectrometry (MS) analysis of the metabolites showed that methylated Cy-3-glu, methylated Cy and glucuronides of Cy are present.

After red wine and black berry fruit, the third popular source of anthocyanins in the diet are **pigmented oranges**. Some varieties of sweet oranges: *Moro, Sanguinello, Tarocco* are characterized by a high content of anthocyanins. These compounds are present both in the juices and the tissues of fruit, and the fruits are commonly called "blood oranges". Red pigmented oranges are cultivated in Sicily (Italy), Florida (USA) and Israel. Citrus fruit and their derived products are widely consumed and therefore may contribute significantly to the total dietary intake of anthocyanins. Cyanidin-3-glucoside (Cy-3-glu) and cyanidin-3- (6"-malonyl) glucoside were dominant anthocyanins

in all the pigmented varieties[88]. Differences between varieties were observed in anthocyanins and hesperidin (flavanone glycoside) content. Quantitatively, the major antioxidant component of all orange juices was ascorbic acid, and its concentration was significantly correlated with the total antioxidant activity of the juices.

It seemed interesting to check the absorption of Cy-3-glu from red orange juice. The transport of anthocyanins across the mucosal epithelium of a rat's exerted small intestine was studied and the ability to cross the intestinal wall in its intact form was confirmed. Comparing the rate of Cy-3-glu absorption from a standard solution and from red orange juice it was clearly evident that the **kinetics of absorption is affected by the food matrix**.[89] Studies on quercetin glycosides showed that these compounds are able to interact with the sodium-dependent glucose transport receptors in the mucosal epithelium. Quercetin-3-O-glucoside and cyanidin-3-O-glucoside are structurally similar and the presence of anthocyanin in the unchanged form, as glucoside, may suggest that the glucose transport receptors are also involved in the absorption of these compounds *in vivo*. Another indication may be that the rate of absorption is related to the type of ingested foods or even with the amount of sugar.

Does the absorption of anthocyanins depend on the simultaneous consumption of sugar? The answer is: yes.

Healthy volunteers were asked to ingest 11g of elderberry concentrate (1.9g anthocyanins equivalent to 235 ml fresh juice) on empty stomach[90]. One day the concentrate was diluted with water, the other day it was it was sweet (30 g sucrose). During 6h they were not allowed to eat or drink anything except water. Urine samples were taken every hour and an HPLC method was applied for the detection of anthocyanins. The main anthocyanins that are found in elderberry (*Sambucus nigra*) are Cy-3-glucoside containing one sugar unit and Cy-sambubioside with three sugar units. Using HPLC it was possible to quantify these two main anthocyanins excreted unchanged in the urine (0.003 –0.012% of the oral dose); the maximum of their excretion was after 1 to 3h. **The ingestion of sucrose led to a reduced excretion of anthocyanins.** It is an argument for the hypothesis that the glucose transporters are involved in the absorption of anthocyanins. When they are simultaneously transporting sugars from the sweet beverage, the rate of the anthocyanin absorption decreases.

Are the anthocyanins toxic and how much can be consumed daily?

In the USA, the daily intake of anthocyanins was estimated at 180-215 mg which is approximately ten times more than the intake of other flavonoids (the most popular flavonols quercetin and kaempferol) – 23 mg/day. During the summer season dietary intakes of anthocyanins may exceed 200 mg/day. The inhabitants of the countries in Northern latitudes generally consume more berries, and the consumption of 1/2 to 1 kg per day does not make any harm.

It is difficult to say something about the overdoses of fresh berries since the only known result can be light diarrhea. It is worth remembering that folk medicine used bilberry fruit (and leaves) as an astringent for stomach ailments and…diarrhea. For more than a thousand years people have consumed berries, including bilberry, blueberry, elderberry, cranberry without any limits and considered berries as healthy food. It confirms that **anthocyanins are not toxic to humans**.

An attempt performed on laboratory animals in order to establish the upper daily dose failed because even

...tragastric administration of antho-cyanin-rich extract of Aronia in large quantities, up to 5 g/kg of body weight was not toxic. Mice were given 10 mg/kg of body weight of Aronia anthocyanins (Aronox) for 6 weeks without toxic side effects; they behave normally, ate foods and increased weight. No pathological changes were observed during histological studies of their main organs. **No side effects have been observed after intake of anthocyanins from Aronia.** The highest known dose, approximately 20 g of the chokeberry extract (containing 1.3 g of cyanidin 3-glyco-sides) was consumed daily by the volunteers in the experiments of Kay [Kay, 2004].

Mixed fruit juice

Besides fruits, juices are suitable food products in terms of ingestion of health protective phytochemicals. **The bioactive components may even be better absorbed from juice than from plant tissues, as it was shown for vitamin C.** Juices produced from berries and small fruits are rich in antioxidants and should be popularized. The German Institute of Enology and Beverage Research developed a special antioxidant juice containing: 30% white grape-, 25% black currant-, 15% elderberry-, 10% sour cherry-, 10% blackberry- and 10% Aronia-juice. The mixture contained 415 mg/l of anthocyanins (mainly glycosides of cyanidin and malvidin), 2,470 mg/l of total phenols (as gallic acid equivalents) and 103 mg/l of ascorbic acid. The bioavailability of its most important bioactive compounds and the influence of juice consumption on antioxidant capacity of blood plasma was assessed.[91] After an overnight fasting for 12h six healthy volunteers ingested a portion of 400 ml juice (the control group received water). Urine and blood samples were collected before and post application

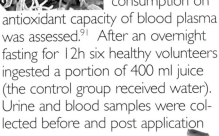

and analyzed.   The mean plasmatic antioxidant capacity of the volunteers increased significantly during the following 2h and dropped back after 6h to initial values. Vitamin C was rapidly excreted in urine after intake, the total excretion within 8h reached approximately 80% of the ingested amount. Its excellent bioavailability and fast excretion rate is well known. Contrary to vitamin C, urinary anthocyanin excretion was only 0.06%, with a maximum excretion after 2h.

The experiment clearly demonstrated that consumption of a single large dose of antioxidant juice produces a significant (about 30%) but temporary rise in plasma antioxidant capacity.

A decrease in plasma malondialdehyde (MDA) level (by 18%) and an increase in plasma antioxidant capacity indicated an improvement in the antioxidant status. The ingredients of the juice, anthocyanins and other polyphenols as well as vitamin C are available for humans and active as antioxidants *in vivo*. The mixture of berry juices meets the EU criteria of "functional food" and may be recommended as a healthy beverage.

Can polyphenolic "phytamins" such as anthocyanins replace vitamin E or C?

Northern countries generally have a habitually low consumption of foods rich in antioxidant micronutrients. A majority of the population may not achieve the recommended daily allowance for vitamin E or C due to the expense and lack of available fresh fruits and vegetables. An important source of antioxidant-rich food may be locally grown berries (raspberries, cranberries, blueberries and other berries rich in anthocyanins).

It seemed interesting to establish whether anthocyanins could act as putative antioxidant micronutrients. Rats were maintained on vitamin E-deficient diets for 12 weeks in order to enhance susceptibility to oxidative damage[92]. The vitamin E deficiency was associated with a 30% decrease in plasma antioxidant capacity and with an increase in hydroperoxides and 8-Oxo-dG (biomarker of oxidative DNA damage) in the liver. After 10 weeks, the rats were offered the diet containing either vitamin E or the dry anthocyanin extract (1 g/kg diet) for an additional 2 weeks. Repletion with vitamin E rapidly reversed the biochemical symptoms of its deficiency. The consumption of the anthocyanin-rich extract also moderated elevated indices of oxidative DNA damage. Whether this effect is ascribed to direct free radical scavenging or to up-regulation of DNA repair mechanisms and antioxidant enzymes is not clear. The effects confirm the antioxidant activity of anthocyanins *in vivo*. The ability of strongly polar anthocyanins to substitute for vitamin E, a lipophilic antioxidant, is apparent.

The mechanism may be analogous to the ability of vitamin C to protect membranes; neither vitamin C nor anthocyanins are strongly inter-calated in the cell membranes but they may regenerate oxidized forms of vitamin E as well as chelate transition metal ions involved in radical reactions.

Besides anthocyanins, catechins constitute a second important group of bioactive compounds in Aronia berries. Could they be detected in biological fluids?

The extracts from berries contain catechins, present as monomers (-)-epicatechin and (+)-catechin, dimers (procyanidins B2), oligomers and higher polymers. Studies on the absorption and metabolism of monomeric catechins go back to the 1950's; the early work indicated that the potential pathways of metabolism are glucuronidation and sulfation.

Catechins are somewhat unusual between flavonoids because they are not present as glycosides in the diet and a sugar moiety does not play a role in their absorption.

Metabolism of (+)-catechin and (-)-epicatechin was been investigated in 1999 in rats[93]. The animals were given a dosage of 100 mg/kg of body weight and the truly active compounds in the urine, bile, and plasma were detected by HPLC, MS and NMR. The plasma concentrations of intact catechin and epicatechin were very low, while the concentration of major metabolite reached 6.90 µM and 15.56 µM in 2h after ingestion of (+)-catechin and (-)-epicatechin, respectively. The major antioxidative molecules appearing in biological fluids were identified to be 5-O-β-glucuronides, the other metabolites were 3'-O-methylated 5-O-glucuronides.

In plants, frequently appear the 3-O- and 7-O-glycosides of flavonoids. The selective in vivo modification of catechin and epicatechin at the 5-O-position may be a common metabolic feature in animals. Conversion to 5-O-glucuronides and 3'-O-methyl metabolites attenuate antioxidative activity. Nevertheless, these metabolites would be largely responsible for the antioxidative defense character added to the body fluids after consumption of catechins-rich diet.

The chemical structure of other (-)-epicatechin metabolites present in blood, tissues, and urine remains unclear. In the study performed in 2003[94] three metabolites from human urine were purified and analyzed by NMR and LC-MS: (-)-epicatechin-3'-O-glucuronide, 4'-O-methyl-(-)-epicatechin-3'-O-glucuronide, and 4'-O-methyl-(-)-epicatechin-5-O-glucuronide. The metabolites purified from rat urine were 3'-O-methyl- and/or 7-O-glucuronides of (-)-epicatechin. These compounds were also detected in the blood of humans and rats.

In the previously published **studies there was no information whether the dimers or trimers of catechins are absorbed. Are dimeric procyanidins such as B2 present in blood?**

After the administration of procyanidin B2 [epicatechin- (4β-8)-epicatechin] the bioavailability and plasma antioxidative activity has been evaluated[95] in rats. Procyanidin B2 is absorbed and excreted in urine, and a portion is degraded to (-)-epicatechin and to the metabolized conjugated and/or methylated (-)-epicatechin.

The problem of the polymeric catechins absorption was assessed using food that is known to be rich in the flavan-3-ol epicatechin and procyanidin oligomers: cocoa and chocolate. Five healthy volunteers consumed cocoa (0.375 g/kg body weight) and procyanidins were detected in blood by HPLC and LC/MS in 1/2h after intake[96]. The maximum concentration (41 nmol/L) of the dimer, epicatechin- (4β-8)-epicatechin was achieved 2h later. Monomeric catechins were also determined: (-)-epicatechin reached concentration of 5.92 μmol/L and (+)-catechin 0.16 μmol/L.

The bioavailability and the biological effects of catechins are poorly understood mainly because of their low concentration in body fluids.

To address these issues, a method based on HPLC coupled with electrochemical detection was developed [Holt, 2002] to determine the physiological levels of epicatechin, catechin and epicatechin dimers. This method allows for the determination of 20 pg (69 fmol; femtomol = 10^{-15}M) of epicatechin, which translates to plasma concentrations as low as 1 nmol/L. The absorption of epicatechin, from an 80-g semisweet chocolate was evaluated. By 2h after ingestion, there was a 12-fold increase in plasma epicatechin, from 22 to 257 nmol/L. Consistent with the antioxidant properties of epicatechin, within the same 2h period, there was a significant increase of 31% in plasma total antioxidant capacity and a decrease of 40% in plasma 2-thiobarbituric acid reactive substances. The plasma epicatechin and plasma antioxidant capacity approached baseline values by 6h after ingestion.

The data supports the concept that the consumption of catechins-rich food can result in significant increases in plasma epicatechin concentrations and decreases in plasma baseline oxidation products.

The presence of metabolites in blood and urine suggests that catechins are metabolized and circulated in the body after administration of catechin-containing foods (although oligomers and polymers have not yet been detected in body fluids).

The antioxidant activity of catechin monomers and procyanidin (dimers to hexamers) fractions purified from cocoa was studied in two *in vitro* systems: liposomes and human LDL. Monomers, dimers, and trimers fractions were the most effective antioxidants when liposome oxidation was initiated in the aqueous phase. When oxidation was initiated in the lipid domains, higher molecular weight procyanidins were the most effective. Reported results[97] give further evidence on the influence of the oligomer chain length on the antioxidant protection by procyanidins.

The conclusion is optimistic: the aggregated data confirmed the bioavailability of chemical constituents of Aronia berries.

Anthocyanins, epicatechin and procyanidins are absorbed from the digestive tract into blood; their presence in body fluids and tissues may modulate metabolic redox processes.

10.2.
SOCIETY WITHOUT ATHEROSCLEROSIS AND HEART DISEASES

The onset of the cardiovascular disease depends on numerous factors that can be modulated by components in the diet. **The intake of saturated fat, insufficient amount of fruit and vegetables, smoking, psychological stress, accelerate the development of atherosclerosis**. Atherosclerosis is a pathological process that results in abnormally thickened regions on the vascular wall. First, low density lipoprotein (LDL) deposits at the arterial wall and is subjected to oxidation. Oxidized LDLs stimulate inflammatory reactions, causing monocytes and macrophages to accumulate and forms foam cells (plaques). The plaques deposit large quantities of cholesterol and their development narrows arteries decreasing blood supply to the heart or brain.

Arteriosclerosis causes cerebrovascular and cardiovascular disease leading to ischemic stroke and myocardial infarction, respectively, and thereby causes more that 40% of all deaths in the Western civilization.

The risk of the cardiovascular disease decreases by lowering cholesterol and triglycerides in blood and inhibiting the oxidation of LDL. The intake of antioxidants hinders the formation of atherogenic plaques through decreasing the concentration of lipid peroxides and oxidized lipids. Elevated levels of lipid peroxides, hydrogen peroxide and decreased superoxide dismutase (SOD, antioxidant enzyme) have been observed in hypertensive patients. There is growing evidence that oxidative stress contributes to the pathogenesis of hypertension. The balance between vasoconstrictors and vasodilators such as NO and oxygen radicals contribute to vascular resistance and to endothelium-dependent contraction.

Antioxidants can be useful in the protection and restoration of endothelial function, produce a relaxant effect and improve platelet aggregation.

Platelets produce significant amounts of ROS (particularly superoxide anion), which can modify their functions including surface markers expression and aggregation. Several studies showed the effects of antioxidant-rich extracts (grape seeds, pomegranate, red wine) on human platelets.

The influence of the extracts of *Aronia melanocarpa* berries on platelet superoxide production and platelet aggregation was studied[98] in 2006. The extracts caused concentration dependent decrease in superoxide production only in patients with cardiovascular risk factors, while no effect was observed in the control group. However, **Aronia extracts exerted significant concentration dependent anti-aggregatory effects** in both studied groups, which indicated that these effects may be independent of the ability to modulate superoxide production. Anti-aggregatory effects appear to be independent of platelet NO release. The mechanisms remain unclear but may be partially mediated by polyphenols acting as ROS scavengers. Anti-platelet effects of *A. melanocarpa* extracts, particularly in patients with significant cardiovascular risk factors, create an opportunity for

development of novel treatment strategies.

In patients with cardiovascular disease treated with statins, the reduction in the incidence of re-infraction or cardiovascular mortality is not only related to LDL-cholesterol lowering effect but also to decreasing of C-reactive protein (CRP) level. The use of moderate doses of statins in combination with natural antioxidants, could represent an alternative therapeutic approach.

In 2007 a study was performed[99] to verify the hypothesis that a reduction of oxidative stress using polyphenols from chokeberry (*Aronia melanocarpa* E) in patients with the history of myocardial infraction, treated with statins, could result in an additional decrease in cardiovascular risk markers. The patients (44) who survived infraction and had received statin (simvastatin) therapy for at least 6 months were given either 3 x 85 mg/day of chokeberry extract or placebo for a period of 6 weeks. The extract (dietary supplement "Aronox") contained anthocyanins (25%), monomeric and oligomeric procyanidins (50%) and phenolic acids (9%). No effect of chokeberry extract on the BMI, lipid, lipoprotein, homocysteine and glucose levels was found. **However, a highly significant lowering of systolic and diastolic blood pressure by an average of 11.0 and 7.2 mmHg was observed in supplemented persons**. Such effect was not obtained in the placebo group. In patients treated with statins and chokeberry extract, the ox-LDL, interleukin-6 and CRP levels were reduced. The effect is probably related to a significant reduction of oxidative stress. The experiment should be considered a pilot one because it was performed for a short period of time and with a relatively small number of patients. Nevertheless, in view of the fact that chokeberry flavonoids reduce the severity of inflammation, regardless of statins, they can be used clinically for secondary prevention of ischaemic heart disease.

Epidemiological studies showed that the consumption of fruits and vegetables is related to the reduced risk of cardiovascular disease and the flavonoids content of foods is a major dietary factor responsible for this protective effect. These studies concentrate on limited number of food items (popular fruits, vegetables and beverages such as green tea and red wine). The importance of small fruits and berries have been underestimated although they contribute remarkably to the Northern countries diets, and are rich in flavonoids.

Can the berries protect human LDL for oxidation *in vitro* and exert a potential health effect *in vivo*?

The antioxidant activity of phenolic compounds present in berries was investigated by two *in vitro* oxidation assays: the human low density lipoprotein (LDL) and lecithin liposomes.[100] LDL oxidation was inhibited by 53.9-83.9% by the phenolics extracted from fresh fruits and the percentage inhibition of oxidation decreased in the following order:

Blackberries (Rubus fructicosus) > red raspberries (Rubus idaeus) > sweet cherries (Prunus avium) > blueberries (Vaccinium corymbosum) > strawberries (Fragaria ananasa).

All berries inhibited LDL and liposome oxidation, the extract of blackberries was significantly more active than others and in both oxidation systems strawberries exerted the weakest antioxidant activity. To explain the differences in antioxidant activity of berries the compositional data and the activities of the phenolic compounds may be of importance. The interpretation is hampered by the fact that phenolic compounds were tested as their free forms (aglycones), whereas in berries they exist either bound to sugars or as esters. In the LDL oxidation, the antioxidant activity of berry extracts was related to the presence of anthocyanins, the predominant compounds in all berries (except sweet cherries). The highest amount of anthocyanins was found in blackberries (7,650 mg/kg).

Aglycones of anthocyanins, the anthocyanidins were shown to effectively inhibit LDL oxidation, and antioxidant activity decreased in the order:

delphinidin > cyanidin > malvidin > pelargonidin

This is in agreement with the general tendency that compounds bearing more OH groups (delphinidin has six) are usually more effective antioxidants. The above order is consistent with the high antioxidant activity toward LDL for blackberries, which contain the highest amount of cyanidin glycosides (cyanidin has five OH groups, its mono- glycosides four) and with the low activity of strawberries, which are rich in pelargonidin-3-O-glucoside (three OH groups).

The three types of antioxidants: anthocyanins, flavan-3-ols and hydroxycinnamic acids inhibit liposome oxidation, but the activity is different from that in LDL oxidation. In the liposomes, the antioxidant activity of the berry extracts correlated with the amount of hydroxycinnamates. The extract of sweet cherries, which is low in anthocyanins and high in hydroxycinnamates, was the most active. The study confirmed that berries contribute a significant source of phenolic antioxidants that may have potential health effects.

Anthocyanins exist in the aqueous phase as a mixture of four species, the concentrations of which depend on pH. Do they have antioxidant properties? In grapes and wines anthocyanins are in the flavylium form but during digestion they may reach higher pH. Quinoidal-base or chalcone can be absorbed from the gut into the blood.

The pH-transformed forms of malvidin and malvidin-3-O-glucoside, the pseudo-base and quinoidal-base remained active and were effective antioxidants in model systems of lipid peroxidation. The bases of malvidin-3-glucoside act better than the aglycones, it may be due to a better interaction of the glucoside with proteins.[101] The antioxidant activity of anthocyanins is strongly affected by the system (cytosol, liposome, membranes, LDL) and catalysts used. Additionally, antioxidant effectiveness may be of limited relevance to human nutrition if the bioavailability of these antioxidants is very low.

10.3.
FIGHTING AGAINST CANCERS

Some carcinogenic factors are present in our environment and are "natural", such as the UV radiation from the sun while others are produced by industrial civilization (air pollution, exhaust gases, products of chemical industry, heavy metals). Living in a city it is difficult to avoid them, because we have to walk along streets with heavy traffic or eat foods with preservatives and artificial colors. Poor diet and cigarette smoking promote cancer development: 30-35% of cancers are diet-related and another 30-35% of all cancers are tobacco-related. Cancer is also related to age, since almost 70% of all cancer deaths occur after the age of sixty-five, and cancers of the prostate, stomach and colon have the highest rates between the ages of sixty and eighty. Next, a sedentary life style is associated with a higher risk of many cancers (the colon, prostate, breast and lung). The cancers of the digestive tract (and also of breast, endometrium and prostate) are linked to dietary habits and especially to high consumption of pickled and salted foods, nitrates and nitrosamines, mycotoxins, fried foods and alcohol.

It is well known that the incorporation of a higher proportion of fruits and vegetables in the diet may help fight cancers. Following one of the more healthy diets may be valuable: Mediterranean (much fruit and vegetables, olive oil), Asian (high consumption of soy products) or vegetarian (almost exclusively plant-derived foods).

It is interesting that the risk of some diet-related cancers is low in Japan, while the Japanese living in Hawaii are subject to an increased risk. After a single generation in America, the cancer incidences resemble that of the host population. The Japanese start to eat the same diet most Americans normally eat: fried potatoes and hamburgers, bacon and mayonnaise sandwiches, e.g., foods rich in saturated fat, carbohydrates and simple sugars, low in dietary fibers and antioxidants.

Food-related mutagens are: polycyclic aromatic hydrocarbons, heterocyclic amines formed during cooking, fungal toxins including aflatoxins and preservatives such as N-nitroso compounds.

It is reasonable to avoid fried, smoked or canned meat and to consume dietary protective substances from plant foods: herbal spices as preservants, cruciferous vegetables (broccoli, cabbage, cauliflower), fruits and berries (Aronia), supplements with microelements (selenium).

A factor that plays a role in cancer development is the intestinal microflora. Lactic acid producing bacteria (probiotic) are able to decrease the genotoxicity of faecal water[102]. It is interesting that the intestinal bacteria are able to modulate the expression of genes in a host, the genes involved in xenobiotic metabolism and mucosal barrier fortification. The individual genetic predisposition, composition of gut microflora and dietary factors interact, inhibiting or increasing cancer risk. One of the key genes affected in cancers is the tumour suppressor gene, p53; it is often mutated in colon cancer. Both, heredity and diet are risk factors. Therefore, people in a high-risk family should pay particular attention to their diet. High beef consumption is a risk factor and cruciferous vegetables appear protective in cases with p53 over-expression.[103]

Nutrigenomics is an emerging science defined as the interaction between nutrition and an individual's genome. It combines food science and modern molecular genetic research, including: nutrigenetics, nutritional epigenomics, nutritional transcriptomics, proteomics and metabolomics.

Fruits, vegetables and whole grain cereals are protective against cancers. Proper probiotics and prebiotics (non-digestible oligasaccharides that are substrate for the microflora) may increase the resistance to cancerogenic agents. Recently, the role of other constituents of plant foods has been intensively studied: the role of dietary fibers[104]. Considered earlier only as the ballast materials, slowing down the digestive processes and the intestinal pass, now they become appreciated as cancer preventive agents.

It is apparent that polyphenols exhibiting antioxidant and radical scavenging properties are effective inhibitors of carcinogenesis - polyphenolic compounds may neutralize free radicals before they assert any damage to biomolecules. The accumulation of reactive oxygen species in cells and resulting damage to DNA structure, modification of enzymatic activity, all influence cancer pathogenesis.

Polyphenols protect against mutations induced by different mutagens in cell culture assays, can inhibit the growth of malignant cells and induce apoptosis. Numerous studies showed that antioxidants protect against many types of cancer and at most stages of carcinogenesis.

In the epidemiological studies, the data on nutrition and lifestyles are collected for years and the risk of cancer is correlated with the early observation. From the initiation of pathology to the reliable diagnostics of cancer usually 10-30 years have gone. Such an approach requires large numbers of patients and can take a very long time.

Instead of waiting for clinical symptoms of the disease one can look for a biomarker (biochemical parameter) that reflects the cancer development.

Biomarkers of oxidative damage should be useful, and the determination of 8-hydroxy-2'-deoxyguanosine (8-OHdG) in urine has been proposed[105] as a measure of the "total body" oxidative DNA damage. In cigarette smokers, diabetics and in patients with rheumatoid arthritis or hepatic inflammation the levels of 8-OHdG are elevated in blood cells and urine. Rises in 8-OHdG are not necessarily due to increased rates of oxidative damage; the decreased repair rate is also possible. As yet, we have no clear information on distribution of oxidative DNA damage in the genome.

Nevertheless, agents (fruit and vegetables) that decrease oxidative DNA damage have an anti-cancer effect whereas agents that increase this damage (cigarette smoking, chemical carcinogens, and chronic inflammation) promote cancer development.

Human DNA is relatively well protected from oxidative damage and such factors as the diet or life style do not have significant effect on the DNA of healthy young individuals. However, cancer and other degenerative diseases, chronic inflammation or advanced age result in an increased level of biomarkers of oxidative stress. Several studies have shown that the administration of fruits and vegetables to healthy volunteers decreased the levels of oxidative DNA damage. The trials with single agents such as vitamin C, vitamin E, coenzyme Q10, particular carotenoids or flavonoids gave disappointing results.

Since the antioxidant mechanism of anthocyanin pigments is still controversial, it seemed worth while to evaluate the effects of cyanidin and cyanidin 3-O-glucoside (cy-3-glu) on DNA cleavage, and on their free radical scavenging capacity[106]. **Cyanidin and cy-3-glu showed a protective effect on DNA cleavage**, a dose-dependent free radical scavenging activity and significant inhibition of xanthine oxidase activity. These effects suggest that anthocyanins exhibit interesting antioxidant properties, and could therefore represent a promising class of compounds useful in the treatment of pathologies where free radical production plays a key role.

Since anthocyanins scavenge free radicals and exhibit antioxidant properties, it can be assumed that **anthocyanins may influence genotoxic activity of the mutagens and act as antimutagens**. The term "antimutagen" is used to characterize the agents that reduce the frequency or rate of spontaneous and induced mutations.

There exists a need to reduce genotoxic effects of mutagenic and carcinogenic factors by the regular intake of some antimutagens and the best choice appear to be food products (fruit, vegetables or natural plant extracts) consumed daily.

The influence of the anthocyanins mixture isolated from *Aronia melanocarpa* on the mutagenic activity of some standard mutagens was estimated in 1997[107] with the *Salmonella typhimurium* tester strains (in the Professor Ames's standard test) and on the proliferation on human lymphocytes *in vitro*. The genotoxic agents were polycyclic hydrocarbons benzopyrene and 2-aminofluorene and mitomycin C. In the Ames test, first the mutagenic potency of sole anthocyanin extract was checked. Anthocyanins in the range of 100-2,000 µg/plate did not show any mutagenic activity. The Aronia extract poured onto nutrient agar plates together with mutagen markedly inhibited its mutagenicity. This inhibitory effect was strongly dose-dependent, and the mixture of aminofluorene with anthocyanins was not cytotoxic to bacterial cells. In the mutagens activity test with human lymphocytes the tested anthocyanin concentrations ranged from 1.5 to 25 µg/ml, and the presence of anthocyanins decreased the genotoxic action of standard mutagens. The impact of anthocyanins on the generation of superoxide radicals by human granulocytes was also evaluated; the inhibitory effects were strongly dependent on the concentration of anthocyanins.

The results suggested that the antimutagenic influence of anthocyanins from Aronia is exerted mainly by their free radicals scavenging action. In addition, anthocyanins also decreased the activity of enzymes, which generated the oxygen radicals. Therefore, it is possible that a pre-treatment of cells with anthocyanins induces resistance against oxidative stress.

Oxidative stress causes damaging cellular effects: mutagenicity, cytotoxic, changes in the gene expression, aging and degenerative diseases. Anthocyanins may exert inhibitory influence by reducing oxidative stress and the Aronia extract is a promising preparation for further study on inhibition of experimental carcinogenesis.

The commercially prepared grape (*Vitis vinifera*), bilberry (*Vaccinium myrtillus L.*), and chokeberry (*Aronia melanocarpa E.*) anthocyanin-rich extracts were investigated for their potential chemopreventive activity against colon cancer[108]. Extracts were semi purified and characterized by high-pressure liquid chromatography, spectrophotometry, and colorimetry. The growth of colon-cancer-derived and nontumorigenic colonic cells exposed to extracts (10-75 µg of monomeric anthocyanin/mL) were monitored for up to 72 h.

All extracts inhibited the growth of cancer cells, with the chokeberry extract being the most potent inhibitor. Cancer cell growth was inhibited approximately 50% after 48h of exposure to 25 µg/mL chokeberry extract. Most importantly, the growth of nontumorigenic cells was not inhibited at lower concentrations of all three extracts, illustrating greater growth inhibition of colon cancer, as compared to nontumorigenic cells. The varying compositions and degrees of growth inhibition suggest that the anthocyanin chemical structure may play an important role in the growth inhibitory activity.

Based on previous observations that tart cherry anthocyanins and their aglycone, cyanidin, can inhibit cyclooxygenase enzymes, the experiments have been conducted to test the potential of anthocyanins to inhibit intestinal tumour development in mice and growth of human colon cancer cell lines.[109] Mice consuming the cherry diet, anthocyanins, or cyanidin had significantly fewer and smaller cecal adenomas than mice consuming the control diet. Colonic tumour numbers and volume were not significantly influenced by treatment. Anthocyanins and cyanidin also reduced cell growth of two human colon cancer cell lines (the IC (50) of anthocyanins and cyanidin was 780 and 63 µM for HT29 cells, respectively and 285 and 85 µM for HCT116 cells, respectively).

The results suggest that tart cherry anthocyanins and cyanidin may reduce the risk of colon cancer.

To investigate anti-cancer effect of anthocyanidins, induction of apoptosis was tested in human promyelocytic leukaemia cells (HL-60), which is a valid model for testing antileukemic or general antitumoral compounds[110]. Of six anthocyanidins representing the aglycones of most of anthocyanins, only those with an ortho-dihydroxyphenyl structure on the B-ring induce apoptosis, suggesting that this structure may contribute to the induction of apoptosis. Delphinidin, the most potent inducer, causes apoptosis in a time-dependent and dose-dependent manner. The efficacious induction of apoptosis was observed at 100 µM for 6h. Concomitant with the apoptosis, delphinidin stimulates JNK (c-Jun N-terminal kinases) pathway activation including JNK phosphorylation and c-jun gene expression, and activates caspase-3. Antioxidants including N-acetyl-L-cysteine and catalase effectively block delphinidin-induced JNK phosphorylation, caspase-3 activation, and DNA fragmentation. Moreover, anthocyanidins directly cause HL-60 cells to generate intracellular hydrogen peroxide. Thus, anthocyanidins may trigger an apoptotic death program through an oxidative stress-involved JNK signaling pathway.

The induction of apoptosis by anthocyanins may be the pivotal mechanism by which its chemopreventive action against cancer is based.

Anthocyanin extract from Aronia may be helpful as a support for anti-cancer therapy. During intracellular processing of alkylating agents capable of cross-linking the DNA the toxic free radicals could be generated. Anthocyanins are able to decrease the side effects after cyclophosphamide therapy and maintain the activity of enzymes: superoxide dismutase, catalases, and adenosine deaminase.

Antiproliferative activities of common fruits were determined using human liver cancer (HepG$_2$).[111] Soluble free phenolics were extracted from fresh fruits, and the cells were grown on media containing different concentrations of fruit extracts. Among the 11 selected fruits, cranberry, lemon, apple, strawberry, red grape, banana and grapefruit showed relatively potent antiproliferative activities on HepG$_2$ cells in a dose-dependent manner. The antiproliferative activity followed the order:

cranberries > lemon > apples > strawberries > red grapes > banana > grapefruit > peach

Antiproliferative activity was measured as median effective dose (EC50), low dose means strong activity. The extract of cranberry has the highest antiproliferative activity, with the lowest effective dose of 14.5 mg/ml whereas the value for banana is 110.1 mg/ml. The extracts from orange, pear and pineapple had no antiproliferative activities.

There was a linear relationship (R^2=0.978) between total phenolic content and antioxidant activity in the extracts of fruits, but there is no significant relationship between the total antioxidant activity and antiproliferative activity. The extracts of fruits showed potent antioxidant activities (expressed as vitamin C equivalent):

cranberry > apple > red grape > strawberry > peach > lemon > banana > orange > grapefruit > pineapple

One would expect that antiproliferative activities would correlate with antioxidant activities. The combination of phytochemicals and synergistic mechanism in the food matrix may be responsible for the antioxidant activities. Vitamin C is usually considered as the major antioxidant in fruits, and in the studied fruit extracts it contributed to only 0.5% of total antioxidant activity. Additionally, phenolics in fruits are both soluble free and bound forms, and the free forms were significantly higher (62-96%) than bound in all tested fruits (except pineapple). The inhibition of cancer cell proliferation by fruit extracts cannot be explained by the total phenolic content in the fruits. Probably, some specific compounds or a class of phenolics was responsible for antiproliferative activities.

The authors propose the "bioactivity index" for dietary cancer prevention, which may be helpful for consumers to choose fruits on the basis of their health beneficial activities. The highest bioactivity index has cranberry, and it decreases as follows:

cranberry (1) > apple (0.42) > lemon (0.36) > strawberry (0.31) > red grape (0.28) > peach (0.18) > banana (0.16) > grapefruit (0.13) > pear (0.10) > orange (0.09) > pineapple (0.05).

Antiproliferative activity of Aronia extract was not tested on HepG$_2$ cells; therefore, bioactivity index cannot be calculated at present. However, antiproliferative activities of its constituents: anthocyanins, epicatechin and its polymers and chlorogenic acid have been reported. Taking into account the high content of polyphenols one may suggest that the index would be close to that of cranberry.

Epidemiologic studies have shown that a diet rich in fruits and vegetables, containing polyphenolic compounds has a beneficial preventive effect in regards to cancers but the mechanisms of these beneficial effects are not known. The purpose of the study performed at the Louis Pasteur University of Strasbourg in France[112] was to define the effect of delphinidin, a vasoactive anthocyanin, on endothelial cell proliferation and migration as well as on in vivo angiogenesis.

Vascular endothelial growth factor-stimulated human umbilical endothelial cell migration and proliferation are potently inhibited by delphinidin. The flow cytometric analysis demonstrated that delphinidin inhibition of proliferation is correlated with the blockade of cell cycle in G (0)/G (1) phase. Delphinidin reverses the vascular endothelial growth factor-induced decrease in expression of cyclin-dependent kinase inhibitor p27 and the vascular endothelial growth factor-induced increase of cyclins D1 and A. Furthermore, delphinidin inhibits neovascularisation in vivo in chorioallantoic membrane model.

Conclusion: delphinidin overcomes the in vitro and in vivo angiogenesis and thus appears promising for the development of an anti-angiogenic therapy.

Epidemiological investigations and animal experiments have indicated that anthocyanins may contribute to cancer chemoprevention. The studies on the mechanism have been done recently at the molecular level.

Current molecular bases for anthocyanidins on several key steps involved in cancer chemoprevention have been summarized[113] as follows:

(i) inhibition of anthocyanidins in cell transformation through targeting mitogen-activated protein kinase (MAPK) pathway and activator protein 1 (AP-1) factor;

(ii) suppression of anthocyanidins in inflammation and carcinogenesis through targeting nuclear factor kappa B (NF-kappa B) pathway and cyclooxygenase 2 (COX-2) gene;

(iii) apoptotic induction of cancer cells by anthocyanidins through reactive oxygen species (ROS) / c-Jun

NH(2)-terminal kinase (JNK)-mediated caspase activation.

This data provides a first molecular view of anthocyanidins contributing to cancer chemoprevention.

Recent studies show that edible berries may have potent chemopreventive properties. Anti-angiogenic approaches to prevent and treat cancer appear to be a priority area in investigative tumour biology. The vascular endothelial growth factor (VEGF) plays a crucial role for the vascularization of tumours. It seemed worth to test the effects of berry extracts on inducible VEGF expression by human keratinocytes.

Six berry extracts (wild blueberry, bilberry, cranberry, elderberry, raspberry seed, and strawberry) and a grape seed proanthocyanidins extract were studied. The uptake of their constituents by keratinocytes was determined using a multi-channel HPLC, antioxidant activity of the extracts was tested by ORAC assay.

Wild bilberry and blueberry extracts possessed the highest ORAC values, followed by cranberry, elderberry and raspberry seed samples (see section 9.3). Each of the berry samples studied significantly inhibited both H2O2 as well as TNF-alpha induced VEGF expression by the human keratinocytes. This effect was not shared by other antioxidants such as alpha-tocopherol or grape seed procyanidins but was commonly shared by pure flavonoids. Matrigel

assay using human dermal microvascular endothelial cells showed that edible berries impair angiogenesis.

Neither anthocyanins of Aronia nor polyphenols of tea are "magic bullets" against cancer and cannot replace the therapy proposed by a physician. However, both may protect from cancer development and may support and regulate endogenous defense systems. At present their role as preventing agents is promising and relatively well documented.

10.4.
NEUROPROTECTIVE ACTIVITY OF ARONIA'S CONSTITUENTS

The human brain is a network of nearly 100 billion neurons and supporting glial cells, it comprises only 2% of the adult body weight but utilizes up to 30% of energy (by resting). A high demand for energy is required to maintain diverse and complex chemical processes.

Unfortunately, receptor sensitivity and motor functions (controlling balance, coordination) decline with age, even in the absence of the neurodegenerative disease. Impairment in cognitive behaviors, in particular that required for learning and memory, has been observed in seniors. What is the chemistry behind these processes? A large body of evidence implicate oxidative damage to proteins! Oxidative damage contributes to the pathogenesis of both normal aging and diseases.

Numerous studies have shown increases in the intracellular concentration of oxidized proteins as a function of age. The rate of oxidation of proteins increases dramatically in the last third of life, such that an average of one in three proteins is affected. This has physiologic consequences since modifications can also inactivate enzymes that are responsible for repair. It was demonstrated that not all proteins are uniformly susceptible to oxidative damage; particularly vulnerable are: mitochondrial aconidase, glutamine synthetase and creatinine kinase.[115] Some proteins undergo nitration and became inactivated (manganese superoxide dismutase, prostacyclin synthase). Creatinine kinase may be nitrated and inactivated by peroxynitrite and/or oxidized, and it is key intracellular enzyme regulating energy metabolism. The damage to kinases leads to inactivation of signaling pathways.

The pharmaceutical industry tries to develop some remedies to slow the rate of functional declines associated with aging. Phytochemicals are interesting because they have long been used by folk medicine and now are recognized as antioxidant and anti-inflammatory agents.

The most widely studied is

Gingko biloba and ginseng; the beneficial effects of other plants are beginning to receive increased attention.[116] **Green tea** rich in polyphenols and blueberry extracts containing anthocyanins are also promising and intensively studied. The aged **garlic extract** which contains S-allycysteine, allicin and diallosulfides has been reported to exhibit beneficial effects towards cognitive impairments in mouse.[117]

Studies on animals suggested that dietary intervention might be important for "neuronal health". Interesting experiments were performed on rats, fed from adulthood to middle age with **extracts prepared from strawberry, spinach, and blueberry**.[118] Animals consumed an equal concentration of antioxidants per day (1.36 mmol Trolox equivalents/kg diet). Biochemical parameters known to be sensitive to oxidative stress were determined. Cognition was examined using performance in the Morris water maze, which measures spatial learning and memory: rats have to find a hidden platform that is located just below the surface of the water.

All extracts appeared to be effective in reversing certain age-related deficits in the neuronal and behavioral parameters, and the blueberry extract was the most effective.

Interestingly, extracts of equal antioxidant potency were not similar in their abilities to protect against declines in motor and learning skills. It would suggest that simple measure of antioxidant activity (such as ORAC) is not predictive in assessing the potency against neurological deficits. *In vitro* antioxidant tests of such supplements should be combined with other measures, e.g., decrements in neurological and cognitive functions. There may be other properties (aside from antioxidative capacity) of these extracts that account for their different efficacies, first characteristic feature would be different polyphenolic composition. It was shown that two different cultivars of blueberry, when supplemented in the diet (20 g/kg – diet) also exhibited different degrees of protection against memory and learning declines.[119] It is not surprising when taking into account the differences in polyphenolic profiles found in berries in relation to the place of cultivation, harvesting time and cultivar variety (section 9.3).

An explanation of why the antioxidant properties are not directly related to the effect *in vivo* may be another biochemical mechanism of action.

It was suggested[120] that **blueberry-induced enhancement of memory in aged rats is associated with neuronal signaling** (e.g., extracellular signal regulated kinase) and alterations in neural sphingomyelin-specific phospholipase C activity.

Understanding mechanisms associated with polyphenols neuroprotection is complicated by the lack of information on their ability to enter the central nervous system. The study[121] focused on the potential for dietary flavonoids, and their known physiologically relevant metabolites, to enter the brain endothelium and cross the blood-brain barrier (BBB) using *in vitro* models (brain endothelial cell lines co-cultured with glioma cells).

The citrus flavonoids, hesperidin, naringenin and their relevant *in vivo* metabolites, as well as the **dietary anthocyanins, cyanidin-3-rutinoside and pelargonidin-3-glucoside, are taken up by brain endothelial cell lines from mouse and rat**.

The high apparent permeability of the citrus flavonoids, hesperetin and naringenin, across the *in vitro* BBB model was observed relative to their more polar glucuronidated conjugates, as well as those of epicatechin and its *in vivo* metabolites, the anthocyanins, and phenolic acids. The results demonstrate that flavonoids and some metabolites are able to traverse the BBB, and that the potential for permeation is consistent with compound lipophilicity.

Alzheimer's disease is the most common neurodegenerative disease leading to progressive memory loss and dementia. Characteristic features are senile plaques containing

β-amyloid and neurofibrillary tangles, which occur in pyramidal neurons of the cerebral cortex and hippocampus. There is a lot of evidence implicating oxidative damage in the pathology of Alzheimer's disease.

Increases in 3-nitrotyrosine and dinitrotyrosine were found in proteins from Alzheimer's *post mortem* brain tissue, and a six-fold increase in 3-nitrotyrosine concentrations was detected in cerebrospinal fluid as compared to age-matched controls.[122]   3-Nitrotyrosine is thought to be a specific marker of oxidative damage mediated by peroxynitrite (NO$^{•}$ reacting with $O_2^{•-}$ generates ONOO$^-$), and ONOO$^-$ can nitrate tyrosine or proteins containing tyrosine residues under physiological conditions. Nitrotyrosine was also detected in atherosclerotic lesions of human coronary arteries, indicating that oxidants derived from NO• are participating in atherogenesis. Thus, it is important to inhibit both brain protein oxidation and nitration.

Free-radical induced lipid peroxidation plays an important role in the β-amyloid-mediated neurotoxicity. Tea catechins are strong antioxidants and free radical scavengers of reactive oxygen and nitrogen species, and the main component epigallocatechin gallate (EGCG) may prevent neuronal damage induced by free radical attack. In order to check it, primary culture of hippocampal neuron was prepared from the embryo of rats and the cells were cultured with β-amyloid and/or EGCG (10 μM).[123] The exposure to β-amyloid resulted in increased lipid peroxidation and this effect was significantly prevented by addition of EGCG to the cultured medium.

Phenolic antioxidants including anthocyanins are known to inhibit LDL oxidation and have anti-atherosclerotic activity. **Can they react with peroxynitrite?**

The mechanism for the scavenging activity of ONOO$^-$ by pelargonidin was demonstrated by T. Tsuda.[124] Pelargonidin was reacted with peroxynitrite and the reaction mixture was analyzed using HPLC, the products were identified as p-hydroxybenzoic acid and 4-hydroxy-3-nitrobenzoic acid. Thus, anthocyanins can function as potent inhibitors of the formation of nitrated tyrosine *in vitro*. Anthocyanins are stable under acidic conditions but rapidly decompose at higher pH; they have not been recognized as physiological antioxidants although they are absorbed and show antioxidant activity *in vivo* (section 10.1).

Studies on animals, clinical trials with Alzheimer's disease and aged non-Alzheimer's patients have shown that they respond well to treatment with nutritional antioxidant flavonoids. The daily intake of fruit and vegetables or plant extracts rich in flavonoids may prevent a risk of Alzheimer's disease and slow down its progress.

Parkinson's disease is the second most common neurodegenerative disease which causes a progressive movement disorder. There is a loss of substantia nigra dopaminergic neurons and oxidized proteins (protein carbonyls) were found in all brain regions. It was suggested that a widely expressed genetic defect in the brain may led to oxidative damage and substantial evidence implicate peroxynitrite-induced protein damage. Increased 3-nitrotyrosine level was found in neurons in Parkinson's substantia nigra.[125]

In most neurodegenerative diseases iron accumulates at brain sites where neuronal death occurs. Misregulation of brain iron metabolism and iron metabolism genes has now been intensively studied. The mechanism of iron activity is not clear, but can be related to redox processes: highly reactive hydroxyl radicals ($OH^\bullet$) are formed in the Fenton's (or Haber-Weiss) reaction, mediated by Fe^{3+}. Polyphenols, especially those with catechol-like structure, are well-established metal chelators, and were shown to be efficient in pharmacological interventions (treatment with a copper-zinc chelator markedly inhibits β-amyloid accumulation). They may neutralize the ferric ion to form the redox-inactive iron. Therefore, iron chelation may be a promising approach to neuroprotection in Alzheimer's or Parkinson's diseases. The neuroprotective effect of catechins may also involve the regulation of antioxidant enzymes, superoxide dismutase and catalase. These findings also support the notion that polyphenols might exert neuroprotection independent of their classical antioxidant activity.

Polyphenols offer protection to the cardiovascular system - inhibition of atherosclerosis mean reduction of age-related deficits in oxygen and glucose delivery to the brain by increasing blood flow. This observation highlights possible neuroprotective effects of the plant extracts.

Chronic alcohol consumption is known to cause oxidative damage to the brain. Unfortunately, it is a serious social problem and has to be extensively studied. The human neuronal damage after chronic ethanol consumption are complex and the extent of damage may depend on the type of alcoholic beverages consumed, as well as genetic, environmental and dietary factors. Ethanol influences NO and ROS production in the brain, hydroxyethyl free radicals derived directly from ethanol are very reactive, and may contribute in the enhancement of oxidative damage. Ethanol may enhance oxidative stress through a number of other mechanisms: over-excitation of neurons, loss of Ca^{++} homeostasis, increase in arachidonic acid release and cyclooxygenase (COX-2) activity.

A better alternative is to drink red wine or alcoholic beverages with fruit juices than pure ethanol (vodka) – because antioxidants may counteract free radical cascade.

Possible interactive effects of chronic ethanol administration and grape polyphenols were examined[126]. The supplementation of grape polyphenols to the ethanol diet could completely prevent the decreases in Na, K-ATPase (transmembrane protein, extremely sensitive to lipid peroxidation) and dopamine uptake activities in rat synatposomes due to chronic administration of ethanol. Polyphenolic compounds of grapes have the ability to prevent the neurodegenerative change.

The study showed that a diet with or without polyphenols did not alter significantly any of the neuronal parameters – it means that **sufficient antioxidant defense is available in the normal brain**. Only when this system is being challenged, **subjected to oxidative stress due to toxic doses of ethanol, polyphenols may exert their ameliorating action**.

10.5.
HEALTHY EYES IN COMPUTER SOCIETY

Vision is the most fundamental of our senses; therefore special care should be taken to keep our eyes in good health. Although all parts of the eye are important for perceiving a good image, the most vital layer for vision is the retina. It is essentially a piece of brain tissue that gets direct stimulation from the outside world.

The human retina is an organization of neurons, glia and nourishing blood vessels. In some eye diseases, the retina becomes damaged or compromised and blindness may be the end result. At the center of the retina is the macula, a small area of photoreceptor cells (responsible for turning light into fine detail and color images in the brain). The macula selectively concentrates carotenoids lutein and zeaxanthin, which give it its anatomical description of *macula lutea*, yellow spot.

Age-related macular degeneration, AMD, can occur as a gradual loss of vision caused by irreversible destruction of the macula, it is a common problem of the aging eye and a leading cause of blindness in the world. AMD effects approximately 10% of the population aged 65 to 74 and this number is expected to increase dramatically as the "baby boomers" enter their later years. (Genetic researchers try distinguishing genes that might cause AMD, after which they will develop possible strategies to prevent it). The eye contains large concentrations of molecular oxygen and it has been theorized that its oxidative qualities are partly at fault for the onset of AMD. Therefore, physicians have been looking at the vitamin therapy (A, C, and E) as a possible treatment or preventive measure because they possess antioxidant behavior. It is not known if this is effective in preventing AMD and caution must be exercised when taking large doses. A recent study showed that smokers have an approximately 2.5 times greater chance of developing AMD than non-smokers. Even if a person had quit smoking almost two decades prior to the study there still remained a two to threefold increase in the likelihood of developing AMD. This observation supports the opinion that AMD could be of free radical ethiology.

Lipophilic antioxidants, carotenoids and tocopherols, are important in the prevention of degenerative eyes diseases; depletion of α-tocopherol increased the risk of AMD. [127]

Glaucoma is a group of diseases that can damage the eye's optic nerve and result in vision loss and blindness. Glaucoma is also a common problem in aging, where the pressure within the eye becomes elevated. As the pressure rises, it compromises the blood vessels of the optic nerve head so that these vital cells die. If glaucoma remains untreated, people may miss objects to the side and out of the corner of their eye. Over time, straight-ahead vision may decrease until no vision remains. Treatment to reduce the intraocular pressure is essential in glaucoma. There is no clinical study showing the inhibitory effect of anthocyanins on the progress of glaucoma; however, since the diseases result from blood vessels and optic nerve disorders - the factors maintaining their proper functioning [128] should be beneficial.

Diabetic retinopathy is a side effect of diabetes that affects the retina and can cause blindness. All people with diabetes - both type 1 and type 2 - are at risk. Diabetic retinopathy occurs when diabetes damages the tiny blood vessels inside the retina and usually affects both eyes. Laser treatment for stopping blood vessel proliferation and leakage of fluid into the retina, is the most common treatment at present. Again, polyphenolics improving capillary elasticity may be helpful.

A **cataract** is when cloudiness occurs in the clear lens of the eye. Common cataract symptoms include poor night vision, sensitivity to light, a painless blurring of vision and a fading or yellowing of colors. Cataracts are most commonly caused by aging, but may be related to family history, eye injury and long-term exposure to sunlight. Lifestyle factors also influence their development, e.g., smoking. Cataracts may develop slowly over a period of years. Surgery is usually successful but connected with enormous costs; this accounts for the largest single item of expenditure on the Medicare budget.

There is convincing evidence that cataracts have an oxidative ethiology. The oxidizing agent, hydrogen peroxide, is present in normal aqueous humor at concentrations of 20-30 μM and is raised up to 660 μM in patients with cataract.

Epidemiological studies suggest that delaying cataract genesis may be achieved by the optimization of nutrition. Preventative effects of diets rich in fruit and vegetables, containing ascorbate, tocopherols and carotenoids have been demonstrated.

Vitamin C depletion (serum ascorbic acid level between 2 and 5 mg/l) may occur long-term complications such as increasing cardiovascular and neoplasic risks and cataract. It is also known that the measured levels of ascorbic acid decline with increasing age in the lens. Most studies investigating risk factors for cataract have been conducted in the United States[129], and there is less information on the possible role of dietary factors in European populations. A case-control study was conducted[130] to investigate the association of antioxidant vitamins (vitamins C, E and A,

β-carotene, α-carotene, β-cryptoxanthin, lycopene, zeaxanthin and lutein) and minerals (zinc and selenium), and risk of cataract in a Mediterranean population (343 cases with cataract and 334 age/sex frequency-matched controls aged 55 to 74 years were selected). The results strengthen the evidence for a protective role for vitamin C on the aging lens as this effect was seen in a population in Spain, characterized by high vitamin C intakes.

The new recommended dietary allowance of vitamin C (110 –250 mg per day for an adult) takes these risks into account. An increased risk of a cataract was observed in people with low blood levels of vitamin E. Therefore, antioxidant vitamin therapy (A, C, and E) may be considered as helpful. It isn't known if this is an effective prevention and caution must be exercised when taking large doses. Excessive intake of anything, even if it is good, has the ability to cause harm.

Zinc is an element concentrated in the eye, especially in the retina and macula. It acts as a catalyst in over 100 enzymatic and chemical reactions, which are vital to the retina. Zinc levels appear to decrease gradually with age and many have correlated this with the advancement of AMD. Studies concerning the effectiveness of vitamin and zinc therapies are currently inconclusive. There are several multiple vitamins commercially available for AMD patients. Despite this option, everyone should maintain **a healthy diet, which will adequately and safely provide the essential elements**.

Anthocyanins may replace rutin and its derivatives in the treatment of illnesses involving tissue inflammation and capillary fragility. It is possible that these compounds influence blood vessels maintaining their elasticity, since they protect collagen. Anthocyanosides and catechins diminish the permeability increasing effect of collagenase and accelerate the recovery of normal permeability.

Proteases, and especially collagenase, injected into the lateral brain ventricles of rats are able to increase the permeability of the blood-brain barrier. This effect seems to be related to a less effective enzymatic attack on collagen.

Strong antioxidant properties of Aronia's antioxidants should be effective in preventing oxidative, degenerative changes of rodopsin dye in the retina. It may be an additional mechanism of anthocyanin's activity.

Folk medicine administrated blueberries or bilberries for the therapy of hypertension and blood capillary fragility.

Well known is the observation that during World War II the pilots of British RAF consumed bilberry jam in order to keep proper vision, especially during night flights. The attempts to confirm these observations inspired a series of studies on anthocyanins effects in animals (rabbits) and humans[131]. A majority of works were carried out with the bilberry extract from *Vaccinium myrtillus* (Myrtocyan), containing 36% of anthocyanosides, dominating anthocyanin is Cy-3-O-glucoside[132].

The placebo-controlled trials of *V. myrtillus*-extracted anthocyanosides have been systematically reviewed for the evidence of positive effects on night vision. Thirty trials with outcome measures relevant to vision in reduced light have been found in databases; of these, 12 were placebo-controlled. Four recent trials were all randomized controlled trials and were negative in outcome. The fifth trial and seven non-randomized ones reported positive effects on outcome measures relevant to night vision. The negative outcome was associated with more rigorous methodology but also with the lower dose level and extracts from geographically distinct sources that may differ in anthocyanosides composition.

The hypothesis that *V. myrtillus* anthocyanosides improves normal night vision is not supported by evidence from rigorous clinical studies.

Evidence from methodologically weaker trials and auxiliary evidence from animal studies, trials of synthetic anthocyanosides, and a recent randomized controlled trial of *Ribes nigrum* (black currant) anthocyanosides may warrant further trials of *V. myrtillus* anthocyanosides in subjects with impaired night vision.

The purpose of the study[134] carried out in 2000 was to investigate the effect of bilberry on night visual acuity and night contrast sensitivity using a double blind, placebo-controlled, crossover design. The subjects were young males with good vision; eight received placebo and seven received active capsules containing 160 mg of bilberry extract (25-percent anthocyanosides), one capsule three times daily for three weeks. After the three-week treatment period, a one-month washout period was employed to allow any effect of bilberry on night vision to dissipate. In the second three-week treatment period, the eight subjects who first received placebo were given active capsules, and the seven who first received active capsules were given placebo. Night vision and night contrast sensitivity was tested throughout the three-month experiment.

There was no difference in night vision during any of the measurement periods when examining the average night vision or the last night vision measurement during active and placebo treatments. Thus, the current study failed to find an effect of bilberry on night visual acuity or night contrast sensitivity for a high dose of bilberry taken for a significant duration. Hence, the current study casts doubt on the proposition that bilberry sup-

plementation, in the forms currently available and in the doses recommended, is an effective treatment for the improvement of night vision in this population.

Healthy subjects with normal or above average eyesight were tested in 11 of the 12 trials. However, it is not rational to expect any significant influence on the eyesight in young car drivers or pilots.

There is an absence of rigorous research into the effects of the anthocyanin-rich extract on subjects suffering impaired night vision due to pathological eye conditions.

Despite the conflicting findings: school children as well as adults watching fast changing images on a monitor or a TV screen can drink a glass of Aronia juice with positive effect to health.

Anthocyanins from Aronia or bilberry may be beneficial for persons who work with computers, make precise drawings by intense light, and for car drivers frequently traveling long distances by night.

10.6.
DIABETES

Diabetes is one of the major diseases concerning the people all over the world. The diabetic state confers an increased propensity to accelerated atherogenesis. In addition to the established risk factors, there is evidence for increased oxidative stress in diabetes, which is manifested by increased lipid peroxidation, increased F2-isoprostanes, increased nitrotyrosine, and increased DNA damage. With regard to diabetes, antioxidants such as tocopherols and ascorbic acid supplementation have been shown to be beneficial. Most importantly, α-tocopherol therapy, especially at high doses, clearly shows a benefit with regard to low-density lipoprotein oxidation, isoprostanes, and monocytes superoxide release. It appears that, **in diabetes, antioxidant therapy could alleviate the increased attendant oxidative stress and emerge as an additional therapeutic modality.**

Increased oxidative stress in diabetes mellitus may underlie the development of endothelial cell dysfunction by decreasing the availability of nitric oxide (NO) as well as by activating pro-inflammatory pathways. In the arterial wall, redox imbalance and oxidation of tetrahydrobiopterin uncouples endothelial nitric oxide synthase (eNOS). This results in decreased production and increased consumption of NO, and generation of free radicals, such as superoxide and peroxynitrite. In the mitochondria, the increased redox potential uncouples oxidative phosphorylation, resulting in the inhibition of electron transport and increased transfer of electrons to molecular oxygen to

form superoxide and other oxidant radicals.

Ample evidence is available suggesting that oxygen stress is present in essentially all tissues and can even be observed in prediabetic states. This suggests that, although hyperglycaemia is largely linked with free radical production, its role may mainly be the aggravation of a pre-existing state. The main debate is about the pertinence of antioxidant therapy since the large scale clinical trials performed recently have essentially failed to show any significant improvement in metabolic disturbances of diabetic patients. No significant associations were observed between serum levels of major dietary antioxidants and retinopathy. However, this conclusion must be tempered by the fact that they have mainly been using single vitamins (E or C). The indisputable involvement of oxygen stress in this disease still leaves hope for alternative therapeutic approaches.

Anthocyanins are effective in decreasing capillary permeability and fragility; therefore, they can prevent progression of diabetic microangiopathy. Microangiopathy – means that the changes occur in the capillary vessels in the eye (retinopathy), foot, kidney or heart.

Hyperglycaemia is considered to be the key causal factor in the development of diabetic complications. The poor glycemic control results in significant changes of erythrocyte membrane fluidity, erythrocyte deformability and changes of antioxidant status. Nonenzymatic glycation and glycoxidation with cascade of free radical reactions, oxidative and carbonyl stress may play an important role in the development of diabetic micro- and macrovascular complications. The serum levels of specific and non-specific advanced glycation end products (AGE) have been found elevated in Type 1 and Type 2 diabetic patients.

The levels of these products may serve as a useful biochemical marker for monitoring the progression of diabetic complications and pathological processes. The accumulation of AGEs on tissue proteins increases with the pathogenesis of diabetic complications and atherosclerosis. AGEs are believed to induce cellular oxidative stress through the interaction with specific cellular receptors. The carbonyl stress-induced tissue damage is caused by AGE precursors formed by hyperglycaemia, hyperlipidemia, nonenzymatic glycation, peroxidation of lipids and metabolism processes. The toxic effects of AGE precursors cannot be directly antagonized by antioxidants. Only a small number of biological carbonyl scavengers, such as glutathione, have been identified to date. Studies *in vitro* showed that AGE inhibitors also display the antioxidant and transition metals chelating activity. Therefore, the supplementation with antioxidants could be a complementary treatment in diabetic patients.

It has been postulated that enhanced generation of reactive oxygen species (ROS) may take part in a pathogenesis of diabetic microvascular complication - retinopathy. Both oxidative stress and the accumulation of advanced glycation end-products appears to promote the apoptosis of retinal microvascular cells, and antioxidants adjunctive therapies are needed to help in preventing or delaying the onset of diabetic complications. The ability of two antioxidants, selenium (ebselen) and lutein (a carotenoid), to reverse these effects was tested.[137]

Antioxidant-rich preparations from Aronia may also be helpful in ameliorating diabetic retinopathy.

Pregnancy complicated by diabetes is an important medical and social problem; in the 1940's the mortality rate related to such cases was as high as 40%. Nowadays, owing to the insulin therapy and intensive medical care, the complications are less dangerous. The problem may increase with the epidemy of obesity, like in Texas, USA where ca. 11% of women are obese and diabetic (in Europe only 0.3 to 6%).

Pawlowicz at al.[138] conducted an experiment involving a group of 105 pregnant women (on the turn of trimester two) with intrauterine growth retardation (IUGR). The authors attempted to determine the influence of the anthocyanin extract from chokeberries on the generation of autoantibodies to oxidize low-density lipoprotein (oLAB) in pregnancies complicated by IUGR. Fifty women were administrated anthocyanins and fifty-five were given placebo, sixty healthy pregnant women served as the control group. The level of oxidative stress was measured by the serum concentration of autoantibodies required to oxidize LDL. In the anthocyanin group the oLAB titres decreased from 1,104 mU/ml before the treatment to 726 mU/ml (the contol group: 601-614 mU/ml), whereas in the placebo group titres showed a slightly increasing trend. The results showed that the natural anthocyanin extract could be useful in controlling oxidative stress during pregnancies complicated by diabetes.

The effect of anthocyanins from the Cabernet red wine on the course and intensity of symptoms of experimental diabetes was investigated[139] in rats. The anthocyanin pigments prevented the generation of oxygen free radicals and decreased the peroxidation of lipids. The simultaneous daily administration of anthocyanins and streptozotocin to rats substantially decreased sugar concentrations in the urine and blood serum. Anthocyanins also inhibited the loss of body mass caused by injections of streptozotocins.

The ability of anthocyanins (cyanidin-3-glucoside, delphinidin-3-glucoside, cyanidin-3-galactoside, and pelargonidin-3-galactoside) and anthocyanidins (cyanidin, delphinidin, pelargonidin, malvidin, and petunidin) to stimulate insulin secretion from rodent pancreatic beta cells in vitro have been determined[140]. The compounds were tested in the presence of 4 and 10 mM glucose concentrations. **The results indicated that Cy-3-glu and Dp-3-glu were the most effective insulin secretagogues among the anthocyanins and anthocyanidins**. Pelargonidin-3-galactoside is one of the major anthocyanins, and its aglycone, pelargonidin, caused a 1.4-fold increase in insulin secretion at 4 mM glucose concentration. The rest of the anthocyanins and anthocyanidins had only marginal effects on insulin at 4 and 10 mM glucose concentrations.

10.7.
SKIN CARE

Skin is the largest organ of the body, accounting for about 16% of a person's weight. It performs a vital role as a barrier and a regulating influence between the outside world and the environment inside the body. It controls the body temperature, prevents the ingress of harmful chemicals and invading microorganisms such as bacteria and viruses. There are two main layers of skin: epidermis and dermis. The main skin cell that makes up the epidermis is the keratinocyte, and new keratinocyte cells are being produced constantly. The dermis contains supporting tissues, blood vessels, nerves, hair roots and sweat glands. Throughout the dermis the proteins collagen and elastin, give it strength and flexibility. Collagen is a triple helix formed by three extended protein chains that wrap around one another. Elastin polypeptide chains are cross-linked together to form rubber like, elastic fibers. A reduction in these proteins with age is normal and contributes to the more fragile skin of elderly people.

As an organ permanently exposed to the environment, the skin is often a target for oxidative stress. A part of this oxidative stress is caused by endogenous sources such as neutrophils or pathological processes linked to inflammatory diseases. Ultraviolet light (UV), chemicals and gases may be exogenous causes for oxidative stress in the skin.

Over the course of evolution, the skin has developed a complex defense system to protect the organism from oxidative damage. Skin cells can enlist the aid of such enzymes as GSH peroxidases, catalase or superoxide dismutases, as well as the protective abilities of cutaneous low-molecular-weight antioxidants: vitamin E, vitamin C, glutathione, thioredoxin and β-carotene. An overload of the protective system seems to be responsible, at least partially, for serious skin diseases including the formation of tumours and premature skin aging.

The age-dependent increase of the free radicals production is associated with the accumulation of large-scale mitochondrial DNA (mDNA) deletions. The experiments confirm an age-dependent increase of biomarkers such as 8-OH-dG level in the total DNA of skin tissues of persons above the age of 60 years. Endogenous and exogenous free radicals should be neutralized by enzymes, such as superoxide dismutases (Mn, Cu, Zn-SOD), catalase and glutathione peroxidase in the skin fibroblasts. However, their activities were found to decrease with age.

Elevated oxidative stress caused by an imbalance between the production and removal of free radicals occurred in the skin fibroblast after 60 years of age. [4]

There are three worst aging factors: cigarette smoking, exposure to sunlight and bad nutrition.

Bad food choices over a lifetime can accelerate skin aging and add a variety of disease conditions that spoil the skin appearance. Numerous findings support the role of dietary antioxidants, and especially the persons over 60 should remember about regular fruit-and vegetables intake. The natural defense system of the skin can be supported by the application of low-molecular-weight antioxidants. Basically, there are two different approaches, which should be combined:

- topical administration of an antioxidant (cosmetics: nourishing cream, lotion, tonic, body milk).

- oral ingestion of antioxidants (diversified foods, functional foods, dietary supplements).

The aging skin is frequently treated with cosmetics containing collagen, elastin and lipids, which is not sufficient. Topically applied antioxidants should also be included. The protective effect of three flavonoids: quercetin, hesperetin and naringenin, against UV radiation-induced peroxidation were studied on a model membrane[142]. All three display strong antioxidant activity and prove to protect liposomes from peroxidation. In addition, these flavonoids are able to permeate through the stratum corneum (a main barrier against the penetration of exogenous substances through the skin) and to penetrate into deeper skin layers. Since naringenin and hesperetin have significantly higher percutaneous absorption than quercetin, they should be better candidates for employment as protective agents against UV radiation-induced skin damage. The skin absorption of drugs is determined by lipophilicity and other physicochemical properties, including water solubility, molecular size and diffusion. Quercetin is water-insoluble, and it may explain its poorer capability to permeate through the excised human skin.

The photoprotective potential of carotenoids lycopene and β-carotene, vitamin E and C was tested in human skin fibroblasts[143]. Nanoparticles were used to deliver the carotenoids to the aqueous media of cell cultures. The results suggested that the two vitamins have the potential to be effective protectors at low micromolar concentrations, similar to their level in plasma. The carotenoids must be delivered together with vitamin E to prevent formation of oxidative derivatives. Therefore, a combination of natural antioxidant compounds may be envisaged for effective protection.

Bioactive compounds in cosmetics with antioxidant-rich plant extracts (such as the extract from Aronia) contribute to the collagen and elastin regeneration. While the cascades of radicals are neutralized by exogenous antioxidants applied with cosmetics, the skin gains time for repair processes.

Photoaging

The premature aging of the skin repeatedly exposed to ultraviolet radiation from the sun is known as photoaging; such skin is characterized by wrinkles, mottled pigmentation, and is dry and rough.

The spectrum of the ultraviolet light (the wavelengths from 200 to 400 nm) is divided into three sub-bands: A, B & C.

- UVA: at wavelengths of 320-400 nm accounts for 90% of UV radiation reaching the Earth's surface.

- UVB: 290-320 nm is only 10% of UV reaching the Earth and is absorbed in the upper stratosphere at the level of the ozone layer. UVB is 1,000 times more potent in causing sunburn (erythema) than UVA and is largely responsible for skin cancer.
- UVC: 200-290 nm is absorbed in the upper atmosphere, but would cause severe cellular damage if it reached living organisms.

Both UVA and UVB are responsible for the effects of photoaging. UV radiation causes destruction of the outermost lining of the skin (epithelium) as well as damage to the deeper structures. The degradation of endogenous type I collagen fibrils was shown to increase by 58% in irradiated skin, as compared with nonirradiated. Collagenase and gelatinase activity remained elevated for several days after exposures to ultraviolet irradiation, as compared with baseline levels.

Adopting a healthy life style has become a priority for many people of all ages. Exercising outdoors: skiing in the high mountains, playing on the beach in the fresh air and sunshine are popular. **However, excessive sun exposure has long reaching consequences that affect both appearance and health.**

Photodamage begins in infancy - 50% of an individual's ultraviolet light exposure occurs before the age of 18 years. Some dermatologists predict that skin cancer will become the most common type of cancer, and malignant melanoma will become the leading cause of death from skin cancer. Australia has the highest incidences of skin cancer in the world; it concerns up to 2.5% of men and 1.7% of women. A similar situation exists in the USA. Despite the continuing public health education programs, the media constantly showing "healthy tans" and the result is a poor message. Dermatologists alert that there is no such thing as a healthy tan.

The best way to prevent sun damaged skin and skin cancer is to limit or modify the exposure. Sun light, like other forms of radiation, has cumulative effects - the more they are exposed, the more damage is done; therefore:

- avoid tanning between noon and 4 pm
- use hats, sunglasses and clothing (even very thin cotton provides an effective barrier to sunlight)
- apply sunscreen (liberally and frequently) to these areas of the body that are most likely to get burned.

A good sunscreen will provide protection against both UV-A and UV-B light. The sun protection factor (SPF) reflects how many times better the sun protection is over unprotected skin (the higher the SPF number the better). For example, a SPF factor of 15 means that in 15 hours of sun exposure the skin "sees" the same amount of sun as in one hour without protection.

Sunscreens can be divided into two main types:

- Physical: opaque pastes and creams that reflect or scatter incident UV, for example zinc oxide (transparent, micronized form of ZnO is incorporated into a number of other skin products)

- Chemical: act by absorbing UVB; examples: para-aminobenzoic acid (PABA) and its esters, salicylates, cinnamates, anthranilates and the benzophenones. These com pounds absorb wavelengths from 250-365 nm.

It is worthy to note that polyphenolic compounds have a maximum absorption in UV range (280 nm). When applied topically they act as chemical sunscreens (additionally to the radical scavenging activity).

The increased incidence of cutaneous malignancy from sun exposure and increased UV radiation caused by a thinning of the stratospheric ozone now becomes a major health concern. The amount of UV-B radiation in natural sunlight is dependent upon the concentration of ozone molecules in the atmosphere.

More than 25 years ago, scientists first hypothesized that human activi

ties could harm the stratospheric ozone layer. Large seasonal depletion of ozone, called the "ozone hole" is observed each year over Antarctica and downward trends of about 4-5% per decade have been observed at mid-latitudes in both hemispheres. The weight of evidence indicates that these losses are due in large part to human-produced chemicals. The monitoring data shows that the growth in concentrations of ozone-depleting chemicals in the atmosphere is slowing, consistent with their declining production. However, the maximum ozone depletion and increase in UV-B radiation is likely to occur within the next 10 years. Thereafter, the ozone layer is expected to slowly recover.

Even a small increase in UV-B radiation is likely to influence human health. The best-known harmful effects are cancers of the skin and eye damage, including cataracts. UV-B radiation contributes to the development of melanoma skin cancer: for each 1% reduction in ozone, the incidence of non-melanoma skin cancer will increase by 2%. Each 1% decrease in ozone concentration is estimated to increase the incidence of cataracts by about 0.5%.

Increased UV-B radiation could increase the severity of some infections in human populations. Furthermore, skin pigmentation does not seem to provide much protection against the immunosuppressive effects of UV irradiation in humans.

Phytochemicals against sunburn

As widely known, an acute exposure to UV leads to an inflammatory response, skin erythema. Epidermal cells exposed to sufficient damage can undergo apoptosis, i.e., "programmed cell death"; this is manifested as "sunburn cells". A reduction in the number of sunburned cells is commonly used as an indication of a protective effect of sunscreens. Application of antioxidants has been demonstrated to reduce the number of sunburn cells, mainly because the free radicals generated by UV can be removed before they cause extensive damage.

The pine bark extract has been used in traditional medicine in Europe and America for inflammatory diseases (among other uses). An interesting experiment was performed in 2001 in Arizona, USA.[144] Young fair-skinned volunteers were given Pycnogenol, the procyanidin-rich French maritime pine (*Pinus maritima*) extract and were exposed to UV radiation (200-400 nm). The extract contained a standardized mixture of monomeric phenols (catechin, epicatechin, taxifolin), larger catechins (procyanidins and oligomers up to heptamers) and phenolic acids and has strong antioxidant properties. Minimal erythema doses (MED) were measured (sites of 1 cm were irradiated for 1 min) twice before supplementation, once after the first three weeks of supplementation and a last time at the end of the study. The participants were given 1.10 or 1.66 mg/kg body weight and per day. An increase in MED was observed after oral supplementation as well as when the dosage was increased (MED was nearly twice the mean baseline). Since the activation of the pro-inflammatory and redox-regulated transcription factor NF-kappaB is thought to play a major role in erythema, the effect was also investigated *in vitro*, in the human keratinocyte cell line. The pine extract added to the cell culture medium, inhibited UV radiation induced NK-kappaB-dependent gene expression in a concentration-dependent manner.

Carotenoids, known as effective antioxidants also increase MED after oral supplementation in humans.[145]

There has been increasing interest in the health benefits of tea, particularly green tea. The consumption of tea could have a protective effect against inflammatory diseases and certain forms of cancer. Inhibitory effects of **black tea and green tea** on UV-related carcinogenesis were studied in mice.[146] Black tea consumption was associated with a reduction in the number of sunburnt cells in the epidermis of hairless mice 24h after UVA+B irradiation. Other indices of early damage were not affected. Neutrophils infiltration, which is due to the increased blood flow in the dermis and can be a measure of skin redness, was slightly lowered by tea consumption. Administration of either green or black tea resulted in significantly fewer skin papillomas and tumours induced by UV- A+B light; this confirms earlier reports that tea consumption can reduce the incidence of skin cancer.

Erythema prevention after UV challenge was observed in humans after oral ingestion of antioxidant-rich extracts. When planning a holiday on a sunny beach one should consume more fruit and vegetables or encapsulated extract, such as pine bark or Aronia's anthocyanins.

A reasonable strategy for skin care can include:

- searching functional (antioxidant-rich) foods in a local supermarket

- asking for dietary supplements with antioxidants in a drugstore

- selecting good quality cosmetics, a skin cream with herbal extracts, vitamin C, E, coenzyme Q10

- protecting the skin against UV (clothing, sunscreens)

Planning our daily meals it is reasonable to take into account the suggestion that a healthy diet should contain dietary plants, which grow in the neighborhood, in the same climate. The macrobiotic diet, which attempts to achieve harmony between yin and yang, is also interesting. Its practitioners use macrobiotics as a tool that allows one to live within the natural order of life, eating a simple, balanced diet. The two food groups: whole grains (should comprise 50–60% of a person's daily food intake) and fresh vegetables (25–30%) are emphasized. Foods considered either extremely yin or extremely yang are avoided. Extremely yin foods and beverages include refined sugars, chocolate, tropical fruits and juices. Detoxifying or anti-aging preparations frequently contain some exotic plants from distant regions: South American or African rain forests, Andean or Tibet. Sometimes it might be helpful.

To learn about new, unknown plants is always interesting but…. **in everyday health care it would be better to relay on native fruits and vegetables. Europeans and Americans should not forget to consume berries.**

10.8.
OTHER DISEASES

Pharmacological effects of the anthocyanin-rich extract from Aronia result from its composition and can be multidirectional. Major constituents are polyphenols: anthocyanins, catechins, hydroxycinnamic acids (chlorogenic acid) with strong antioxidant and anti-radical properties.

Numerous studies confirmed that compounds present in Aronia berries are effective in neutralizing free radicals and reactive oxygen and nitrogen species, which are harmful to our organism. ROS and RNS contribute to collagen degradation, decreased activity of antioxidant enzymes, damage to DNA and proteins, the oxidizing of membrane lipids.

The accumulation of such damages results in pathologies and development of **diseases of free radical ethiology:**

➢ **rheumatoidal arthritis**

➢ **allergies**

➢ **virus and bacterial infections, including influenza (flu) and cold**

Anti-inflammatory drugs (aspirin, non-steroidal anti-inflammatory drugs, cyclooxygenase inhibitors (COX-1, COX-2) are frequently not effective and have numerous side effects. There is growing interest in the utilization of phytopharmaceuticals. Some flav-onoids (such as quercetin) blocked the cyclogenase and lipooxygenase pathways, a flavonoid complex (diosmin+hesperidin) exhibited inhibitory activity on the inflammatory process. Anthocyanins from cherries and berries: bilberries, blackberries, blueberries, raspberries and strawberries were investigated for cyclooxygenase inhibitory activity[147]. Anthocyanins from raspberries and sweet cherries demonstrated 45% and 47% cyclooxygenase-I and cyclooxygenase-II inhibitory activities, respectively. The cyclogenase inhibitory activities of anthocyanins were comparable to those of ibuprofen and naproxen at 10 μ M concentrations.

The results suggest that the consumption of anthocyanin-rich fruits may be beneficial to human health and should be included in a regular diet for alleviating arthritis- and gut-related pain.

Numerous cases where the application of the anthocyanin-rich extract may be beneficial have been recognized by the scientists from previous Military Medical Academy of Łódź (now Medical University) guided by Professor J. Niedworok. The list includes: gastric ulcer, inflammation of pancreas, diabetes, cadmium intoxication, military gases intoxication or radiation sickness. The administration of Aronia anthocyanins to rats before the intraperitoneal injections of Platelet-Activating Factor (PAF) and ceruleine had a benefical effect on the development of acute experimental pancreatitis. The decreased activity of enzymes: α-amylase, adenosine deaminase in the blood serum was observed as well as decreased peroxidation of lipids in the liver, lungs and tissue.[148]

Strong antioxidative properties of anthocyanin-rich extract from Aronia can be beneficial in the treatment of acute intoxications by petrol ingredients or heavy metals (Cd, Pb).

Despite reduction in

cigarette consumption, reduction in fatty food consumption and despite improved screening procedures, cancers of the lung, breast and blood system is on the rise. It is attributed to a combination of environmental chemical factors, imposed on the genetic makeup of the individual.

Anthocyanins from Aronia have been administrated for two months in personnel of gasoline stations, professionals who have to inhale petrol products for several hours per day. The indicators of oxidative stress were reduced: the level of Pb in urine, delta-aminolevulenic acid, concentration of aminoacids and product reactive with thiobarbituric acid (TBARS), nitrotyrosine, 8-hydroxy-2'-deoxyguanosine (8OHdG), from damaged DNA.

It seemed worth administering the Aronia extract to the employees of petrol stations, exposed to gasoline products, heavy metal ions and car exhaust.

Summing up:

• Aronia extract in capsules used as a food supplement is not toxic (no side effects are known), no allergic reaction was observed

• There are no contra indications, also by simultaneous intake of other medications, synthetic or natural

• The extracts of anthocyanins from Aronia are in the drug stores as food supplements, no recipe is required. Fruit products with Aronia: jam, syrup and juice can be found in food shops, from small ones to super-markets. Aronia has beneficial prop-erties in any product; only the concentration of bioactive compounds vary.

• Prevention is cheaper and better than therapy. It is rational to include Aronia products for everyday use. Prevention of degenerative diseases is now more important than therapeu-tical applications (which require further clinical studies).

ARONIA AND THE ARMY

It may be a somewhat surprising connection, but the suspicions that Aronia might be a "top secret plant weapon" are not substantial. Quite seriously, Aronia appears to be an "apparent defense remedy" administrated in some extraordinary situations. It would be much better if such cases would remain fully theoretical. However, some useful information should be kept in mind.

Military Institutes in Russia and Poland investigated the unique properties of Aronia extracts and found that it represents a cheap, readily accessible and valuable material.

The berries of Aronia, anthocyanin extract and other anthocyanin-rich preparations may be useful in the treatment of radiation sickness, acute intoxications by mustard gas and other alkylating agents, benzene hydrocarbons, chlorinated hydrocarbons etc.

11.1.
CHEMICAL WEAPONS

The first large-scale use of chemical weapons, in the modern era, occurred during World War I, on battlefields near Ieper, Belgium. In the course of that war, 100,000 tons of toxic chemicals, such as chlorine, mustard gas and phosgene, were deployed against soldiers and civilians. The horrors of chemical warfare experience caused such outrage that the countries resolved to ban the use of toxic chemicals forever. During World War II, chemical weapons were not used (and after that war the global arms control agenda was busy with the new, nuclear weapon)!

The Chemical Weapons Convention was opened for signature in Paris, January 1993 and entered into force April 1997. It prohibits the development, production, stockpiling and use of chemical weapons. The Organization for the Prohibition of Chemical Weapons (OPCW) in the Hague, established by the convention, is responsible for the implementation of the convention. The total number of ratifications and accessions reached 162; it seems that another world war with poisonous gases is not probable. However:

• some mad religious groups can use chemical agents. In 1995, the Aum

Shinrikyo religious cult released the chemical agent sarin in the Tokyo subway and planned other attacks with chemical agents or weapons in Japan. Thousands were injured.

• these simple chemical substances can be produced by terrorists. The Japanese incident proved how dangerous these weapons could be and how real a threat they posed, especially if they were to fall into the hands of terrorist organizations.

• some countries still store significant amounts of these compounds.

• large quantities are sunken in seas and oceans, and a disaster is near European seashores.

Unfortunately, the Baltic Sea is home to over 300 thousand tons of old chemical weapons. Britain, the Soviet Union and the United States captured these from Nazi Germany. After World War II the allies thought that the best thing to do was to sink them. Poisons like arsenic, sarin and mustard gas are among the weapons in the Baltic. Some bombs and shells under the sea date back to World War I. According to scientists, damage caused by water has permitted poisons to leak out of their containers. Fishing crews have pulled up bombs and shells. Fishing boats do not always obey restricted areas. Nor do they always know where weapons are located. Some people have suffered chemical burns.

The Helsinki Commission (an intergovernmental group that supervises the Baltic Sea environment) has published guidelines on how fishing boats can avoid risky areas. They also advise fishing crews what to do if they pull up weapons. Included is medical advice and information on how to clean boats after such an incident.

High toxicity of mustard gases results from their high reactivity. They form carbonium ion intermediates, which react further with nucleophiles forming covalent bonds (alkylating) with various molecules, including macromolecules such as DNA or proteins. Their toxicity is most pronounced in fast proliferating cells; therefore they could be applied to kill cancer cells.

Alkylating agents, developed from nitrogen mustard gases, produce cross-links between DNA strands or between DNA and other available reactive chemical groups, misreading of genetic code retards cancer cell growth. Alkylating agents, as a class, are now the most broadly used anticancer drugs in the world. They are not cell cycle specific, but still more active in dividing tissues. In recent years, alkylating agents have been increasingly used in dose intensification strategies, such as bone marrow transplant, and have exhibited further promise when used with thiophosphate protection agents. However, a majority of cancers develop resistance to currently available alkylating and platinating agents.

Their molecular mechanism of action has been widely studied, however is not sufficiently recognized. Especially, the modes of protection against by-products of their reactions and the free radical reactions in tissues. Alkylating agents are considered as "radiomimetic" since the action on DNA resembles radiation damages: damages of biomolecules result from free radical reactions. If the mechanisms are similar and involving oxidative stress and free radical activities – then antioxidants should be considered as a remedy.

A reasonable emergency plan in the cases of chemical attack or irradiation accident would be to administrate high dose of effective antioxidants, such as extracts of Aronia or green tea.

Plant extracts can be treated as first aid, and further as dietary supplements supporting a pharmacological therapy.

Chemopreventive properties of the Aronia extract were investigated using two groups of 60 laboratory mice. One group was intoxicated by a 2-chloroethyl-3-chloropropyl sulphide (derivative of mustard gas), the second one obtained sulphide and anthocyanin-rich extract of Aronia.

After administration of sulphide all mice died within 13 days. However, the simultaneous application of anthocyanins reduced mortality by 40% (see Fig. 16). The anthocyanin extract appears to be effective in prevention. Further studies were performed in order to obtain biochemical information of damage and its prevention.

The mice were separated into four groups receiving: i. NaCl solution, ii. Anthocyanins of Aronia, iii. Sulphide

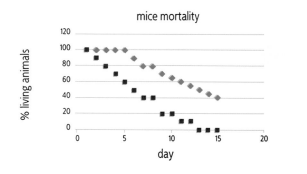

Fig. 16. The protective effect of Aronia anthocyanins after administration of iperite analogue [149]

(iperite analogue) and iv. Sulphide +anthocyanins.

The experiments confirmed that the mechanism of protection is related to the antioxidant activity of the extract from Aronia, it decreased the consequences of free radical damage to membrane lipids. In these reactions the thiobarbituric acid reactive products (TBARS) appear; their concentrations were determined in hemolysate and blood plasma. The animals receiving sulphide exhibited higher TBARS concentration in particular organs: lungs, liver, small intestine; the oxidative processes have been significantly inhibited after the administration of anthocyanins obtained from Aronia.

11.2.
ANTHOCYANINS AND RADIATION SICKNESS

Anthocyanins from Aronia are effective radioprotectors, when administrated orally in proper dosage may have a beneficial influence in radiation sickness.

On April 25-26, 1986 the world's worst nuclear power accident occurred at Chernobyl in the Ukraine. Of the 600 power station personnel and fire-fighters who were in the vicinity of the burning reactor directly after the accident, 134 received doses of 0.7 to 13 Sv. These included the 31 people who died in the first 3 months after the accident

despite intensive treatment. About 800,000 fire-fighters and soldiers were involved in clean-up operations at the reactor complex in the years after the accident. Many of them suffer from conditions including lung cancer and leukemia, cardiovascular diseases and inflammation of the digestive tract.

How does radiation affect the human body? When uranium 235U nuclei are split in a nuclear reactor, various radioactive fission products arise. The most harmful are iodine-131, caesium-137, strontium-90 and plutonium-239. Dust particles in the air with radioactive elements may be inhaled, deposited in the earth by rainfall and water, or enter the food chain via plants. When the cells of the body are exposed to such radiation, free radicals are produced. These free radicals or ions may impair cellular function (see chapter 5). Damage may be caused to the DNA in the cell nucleus, which carries the genetic information for cellular replication, structure and function. It is now scientifically recognized that such damage to the DNA can cause cancer and other genetic abnormalities.

• We do hope that no such disaster will occur in the future but there are still numerous nuclear power plants working in Europe. Additionally, now terrorists may realize an attack on nuclear power plant.

• Successful treatment of men should be indispensable in every emergency plan considering accidents and exposures to radioactive radiation sources.

Not all human organs are equally sensitive to radiation. The lymphatic system (lymph glands), bone marrow, intestinal tract, thyroid, female breast and egg cells or the cells of the embryo are considered to be particularly vulnerable to the effects of radiation.

In addition, the accumulation of radionuclides is particularly marked in certain organs. Radioactive iodine is stored primarily in the thyroid; radiation may impair its functions and also lead to thyroid cancer. Caesium-137, which accumulates throughout the body and in specific organs, is also believed to be a potential cause of cancer. Strontium is stored in teeth and bones. Since new blood cells are formed in the bone marrow, this may lead to leukaemia.

People and animals exposed to a high dose of radiation over a short period show acute effects. These are to be distinguished from so-called late effects, such as tumours or genetic mutations, which often only appear decades later.

A dose greater than 0.5 sievert (Sv) is considered to be a high dose of radiation. Above this threshold, adverse effects become apparent immediately or after a few days at most. The immune system is weakened, changes in blood count occur, and the digestive tract, lungs, other internal organs and the central nervous system are all damaged. With absorbed doses of 1 to 2 Sv and above, mortality is expected to be about 20%, according to radiation medicine specialists.

• It is well known that generation of free radicals is a major result of irradiation and many post irradiation damages result from the activity of free radical cascades. The effects were studied in rabbits (27) and mice (100) by Polish scientists from the Military Medical Academy in Lódź[150]. Animals were irradiated from ^{60}Co sources and absorbed a 4 Gy dose. Biochemical exponents of these processes were estimated:

• activity of deaminase adenosine in blood serum and its concentration,

• generation of superoxide anion by peripheral blood granulocytes, and

• chemiluminescence of splenocytes.

• Significant changes in blood composition were observed after exposing animals to radiation. Mean number of leukocytes in rabbits peripherial blood is less than one half of that measured for control group (Fig. 17). Irradiation results in deaminase adenosine activity decrease and the increase in chemiluminescence of mice splenocytes. Generation of superoxide radicals in rabbits blood was observed after irradiation (see Fig. 18). This confirms the operation of free radicals and oxygen active forms after the exposing animals to radiation (4.0 Gy dose).

• The mechanism of protective effect of the anthocyanin extract is probably based on the reduction of oxidation processes. On day four of the observation made on rabbits, a significant increase of enzyme activity was in the group that was getting anthocyanin extract. The stimulated generation of superoxide anion was significantly decreased due to the administration of the anthocyanins.

• Considering all examined biochemical and morphological parameters, one can conclude that the anthocyanin extract (called the anthocyanin dye) and juice have antioxidant properties.

The radioprotective effect of Aronia's anthocyanins has been confirmed in the experiments performed on cells.[15] The cells of green monkey kidney (GMK) are suitable for such experiments since they readily absorb complex of radioactive technetium with 2,3-mercaptothiosuccinic acid ^{99m}TcDMSA (it is a radiopharmaceutic, devoted to detection and diagnostic of kidney morphology and pathology, frequently used for scintigraphy of kidney).

A distinct radioprotective effect on the GMK cells was observed after the addition of cyanidin, its glycosides and the extract of Aronia berries

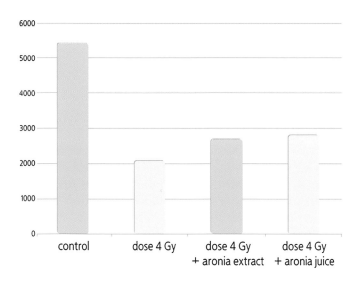

Fig. 17. The radioprotective effect of the Aronia extract and Aronia juice; the mean number of leucocytes in rabbit peripherial blood on the fourth day after absorption of 4 Gy gamma radiation. [from: Andryskowski (1998)]

(Aronox). The effect was estimated as:

1. the cell count after y irradiation emitted by ^{99m}Tc,

2. the determination of dehydrogenase activity (which reflects the level of metabolic damage in cells).

3. the measuring radioactivity of $^{99m}TcDMSA$; it was reabsorbed by cells that survived after first experiment (the cells were subjected again to radiation for 30 min and washed with physiologic NaCl solution). This experiment is a good measure of cell vitality.

extract do not form a natural milieu of kidney cells. However, after irradiation, these compounds provide a protection barrier and diminish the consequences of oxidative stress. Without protective compounds, radiation damage, measured as an increase in LDH is significantly larger (see Fig.19).

It is interesting that the cells which survived the addition of the anthocyanin extract to the culture became more vital and stronger absorbing $^{99m}TcDMSA$. Irradiation of non-protected cells results in three times

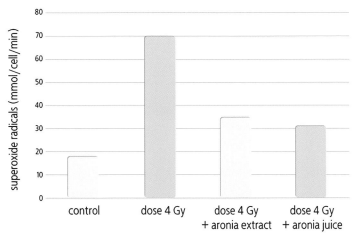

Fig. 18. The radioprotective effect of Aronia extract and Aronia juice simulated generation of free superoxide radicals by rabbit's peripherial blood granulocytes on the fourth day after absorption of 4 Gy gamma radiation dose. [from: Andryskowski (1998)]

A decrease in cell numbers and some increases in dehydrogenase activity may be observed after the addition of anthocyanin solution, without irradiation. Anthocyanins and other compounds present in the

smaller activity, in comparison with control culture. However, low vitality of irradiated cells is two times higher if the cells were incubated with Aronia's extract (see Fig. 20).

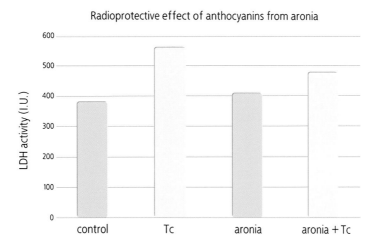

Fig. 19 The radioprotective effect of the Aronia extract on the GMK cell culture: determination of LDH activity after gamma irradiation from ^{99m}Tc.

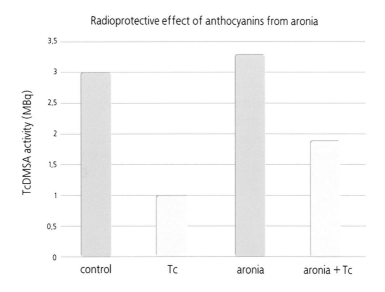

Fig. 20. The radioprotective effect of the Aronia extract on the GMK cells; activity of TcDMSA after repeated irradiation from ^{99m}Tc

These results enable the following conclusion:

Chemical compounds present in Aronia extract are effective antioxidants and free radical scavengers; they are able to counteract oxidative stress in cells after γ-irradiation.

Further experiments are necessary in order to explain molecular mechanisms action of the Aronia extract. The extract is not a single chemical but a mixture of species: anthocyanins, proanthocyanidins and polymers of (-)-epicatechin, hydroxycinnamic acids and many other compounds. Most of them are strong antioxidants and participate in the redox reactions. Besides their reactivity toward free radicals, the reaction mechanisms and activity of particular compounds may be different. It seemed very interesting to find their interactions with cellular enzymes.

Effective radioprotectors that can be administrated after the exposure to radiation are needed to prevent acute and long-term injuries.

Radioprotective effects of some plant extracts have been already reported, for example the extract of **green tea** Camellia sinensis rich in (-)-epigallocatechin gallate[152] and **curcumin** from z Curcuma longa, commonly used in foods as a coloring agent.[153]

Long-term oral administration of (-)-epigallocatechin gallate, major component of green tea, to mice significantly prolonged the life span after lethal irradiation.

Urinary 8-OHdG levels (a biomarker of DNA damage) in rats were significantly increased by exposure to non-lethal doses of γ-radiation; the feeding of dietary curcumin for 3 days before and/or 3 days after the irradiation reduced the elevated levels. Evaluation of its protective action against the long-term effects revealed that curcumin significantly decreased the incidence of mammary and pituitary tumours. Curcuma longa could be useful radioprotector because it is relatively non-toxic.

The radioprotective effects of plant preparations were proven in animals (mice and rats). As compared to laboratory experiments, human studies are very limited.

Clinical trials on the supplementation of nutrients (β-carotene, antioxidants from Ginkgo biloba leaves) have been reported in persons exposed to radiation from the Chernobyl accident. In patients from a radiation-contaminated area near Chernobyl[154] formation of 8-OHdG in bladder urothelium was induced by long-term exposure to the radiation, as a result of oxidative stress. However, the mechanisms of cancer protection by dietary nutrients that can modulate radiation responses are far from clear.

Clinical trials involving persons exposed to radiation during medical treatment evaluated the early effect of diet interventions on chronic radiation damage. Little is known of the late protection effect of antioxidants on carcinogenesis when the damage was initiated many years ago.

A very interesting study was published in 2004 on dietary factors and cancer mortality among atomic-bomb survivors.[155] A cohort of 36,228 persons, who have been exposed to the atomic bombings in Hiroshima and Nagasaki in 1945, had their diet assessed in 1980. The individuals for whom radiation dose estimates were currently available, were followed for 20 years for cancer mortality. Thus, the joint effect of fruit and vegetables intake and radiation exposure on risk of cancer death was examined. Radiation exposure of 1 Sievert (Sv) increased the risk of cancer death by 48-49%. The additive joint-effects showed a lower risk of cancer among those exposed to 1 Sv who had diet rich in vegetables and fruit.

The cancer risk reduction in exposed persons went from 52% (effect of radiation alone) to 32% (product of effect of vegetable and radiation) or to 34% (product of effect of fruit and radiation). In this large cohort of survivors, a daily intake of fruit and vegetables benefited those exposed to radiation in reducing their risk of cancer, at least to the same extent as those not exposed to radiation.

ARONIA IN FOOD, PHARMACEUTICAL AND COSMETIC INDUSTRY

Agricultural companies in Poland produce over 15,000 tons of Aronia fruits every year. The fruits are used for production of juices, jams, fruit-and-herbal teas and excellent alcoholic beverages: Aronia wine and liquor. Food companies from Germany, Scandinavia and Austria are buying fresh fruits from Polish growers. Manufacturers of functional foods from the USA, South Korea and Japan are interested in the Aronia juice concentrate. Poland, now a member of the UE, may easily introduce Aronia products to other European countries and popularize these berries worldwide. The increasing demand for the Aronia berries is a chance for farmers and also for small agricultural enterprises. Aronia berries are a valuable raw material for manufacturing juices and its concentrates because they are characterized by a deeply red, intense color, which is relatively stable in time. Polish manufacturers of Aronia products sell pure Aronia juice, mixed apple-Aronia juice and Aronia jam, which are amongst the most popular products.

Aronia berries are resistant to long transport and can be stored without damage, preserving the whole matrix of bioactive compounds. The berries can be stored up to two weeks at room temperature and 2-3 months in a cool room.

Properly frozen fruit, when held under the right conditions, will maintain its quality for several years. However, the freeze/thaw cycle does cause some damage to the fruit regardless of how carefully the process is done.

Manufacturing of anthocyanin-rich products is not an easy task from a technological point of view. The proportion of fruit, water or sugar is important. Therefore, the blending operation as well as all other operations must be carefully controlled to comply with all regulations and to maintain high quality standards. In order to separate anthocyanins from skins the pulp is heated; the temperature, acidity and access of fresh air should be controlled precisely to avoid the degradation of anthocyanins. A majority of pectins are insoluble in water and are not transferred to Aronia juice, therefore the berries may be pressed easily. The juice is obtained by a mechanical process, according to the Codex Alimentarius Standard.

Fruit waste is a valuable material, containing dietary fibers, pectins and antioxidants. It may be further manufactured in order to obtain a natural dye or add to some food products.

The powdered Aronia fibre is dark violet, almost black; its color suggests that this material is rich in anthocyanins.

The solid state Nuclear Magnetic Resonance (NMR) was developed to study crystalline organic solids but it is a method of choice to analyze powdered, hardly soluble products. The powder is placed in a ceramic rotor and rotated under the "magic angle" of 54° (with respect to the magnetic field direction). This technique, called magic angle spinning, (MAS), enabled observation of narrow resonances for particular carbon atoms in a molecule for solid samples. In the standard ^{13}C MAS NMR spectrum of Aronia fibre (Fig. 21a) major resonances are from cellulose, the dominating ingredient.

However, applying another pulse sequence ("dipolar dephasing", depressing the resonances from carbons linked to hydrogens) one can observe the resonances of quaternary carbons of C-OH groups and identify anthocyanins and catechins (Fig. 21b). Solid state NMR spectra confirm the presence of cyanidin and epicatechin derivatives. The powder obtained from the berry's skin can be a source of these compounds and an additive for production of functional foods (bread, cakes, yogurts).

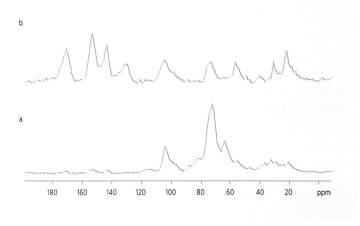

Fig. 21. ^{13}C CPMAS NMR spectra of dietary fibre from Aronia: standard (a) and dipolar dephased (b)

In Warsaw, a bread with Aronia fiber is produced and promoted as "bread for your heart", although it is beneficial also for the digestive tract.

The unique composition of polyphenols caused by Aronia is valuable raw material and should be used as an ingredient **of pharmaceutical preparations and functional foods**. Polyphenols of Aronia consists of anthocyanins, procyanidins, tannins, flavonols and phenolic acids. The high content of chlorogenic acid is an additional specific feature of Aronia berries; its biological effects are beneficial for human health.

Dried Aronia berries (cut or powdered) are a favorable ingredients of fruit-and-herbal teas. The teas are tasty and exhibit strong radical scavenging properties when tested *in vitro* see section 9.2.). Anthocyanin dyes give them the beautiful red color and add significant contribution to the antioxidant capacity. The consumed polyphenolic compounds are those soluble in hot water, absorbed from the digestive tract and further metabolized. For biological activity of Aronia extracts, the monomers and small polymeric anthocyanins and catechins are most important, larger polymers with high molecular mass are not bioavailable because of small solubility in water.

The condensed juice of Aronia with a high content of sugar (also sugar cane) is popular as syrup, used for homemade beverages. Syrups of

Aronia berries may contain other ingredients, such as honey, extract of aloes, vitamin C or minerals (magnesium).

According to manufacturers, the products of Aronia are recommended against hypertension, atherosclerosis, oedema, scalding, varicose veins (haemorrhoids), and inflammation.

Anthocyanin extracts of Aronia are used in cosmetics mainly due to

its strong antioxidant and radical scavenging activity. Gels containing 0.01 to 0.1 % of anthocyanin extract protect skin for UV radiation; they are effective even in the cases when the exposed dose exceeds minimal erythema dose. Polyphenols of Aronia absorb UV radiation (because absorption maximum of epicatechin and its polymers is at 280 nm) and visible light (maximum at 520 nm). Cosmetics with Aronia extract when applied topically act as a light filter. Their protective effects can be compared to those achieved using sun creams with protecting factor (PF) equal to 18.

Aronia at our homes

We do not advise you to produce Aronia juice at home. That type of work requires some machinery and afterwards intense cleaning of the whole kitchen, sprayed in red dots. It is better to buy a bottle or carton of Aronia juice – then the only work is to put ice cubes into the glass. Aronia juice is very tasty and refreshing when mixed (1:1) with apple juice!

Being an owner of 2-3 shrubs of Aronia in the home garden one can pick up several kilos of berries in September and prepare a low-sugar jam with apples or excellent marmalade with plums. Some berries may be left on the shrub, for the birds.

Multi fruit alcoholic tinctures (cherry, black or red currants, raspberries) and fruit wines gain a beautiful color and an interesting taste when Aronia berries are added.

At my home, I freeze Aronia in small plastic bags and store them for several months in the freezer. A portion of Aronia berries mixed with sugar and yogurt is excellent as a healthy dessert for cold winter days.

"ANTIOXIDANT PARADOX" AND MORE

French paradox" was mentioned several times in previous sections. Similar paradoxical findings and events are summarized below.

1. "French paradox I – III".

The discovery that the intake of saturated fat among the French is similar to that of other developed countries while the mortality rate connected with the death from coronary disease in France is only one third of the average, has become known as the **"French paradox"**. However, this well-known paradox has further versions (according to Professor Brouillard):

- a discovery that red wine has health beneficial effects may be called the **"French paradox I"**.

- the **"French paradox II"** is that the Pinot Noir vine is at the origin of the world's best red wines.

- wine pigments vitisins, responsible for long lasting color of red wines are the next French paradox, the **"French paradox III"**. These species may also be responsible for the beneficial effects brought to human health.

2. "Red wine antioxidant paradox".

The interest in the wide use of red wine antioxidants for the prevention and treatment of human diseases has been called the **"red wine antioxidant paradox"**. An avalanche of papers on red wine and its constituents appeared in scientific literature.

3. "Press & TV antioxidant paradox".

Antioxidants stimulate keen interest in the mass media. The reason is obvious: antioxidants are not only involved with major diseases (heart infarct, cancer), but also with anti-aging strategy (cosmetics, youth elixir).

4. "Antioxidant vitamin paradox".

The more vitamins (A, C, E) does not mean the better. An observation, that high doses of antioxidant vitamins, especially those soluble in lipids exert pro-oxidant action is called the **"antioxidant vitamin paradox"**.

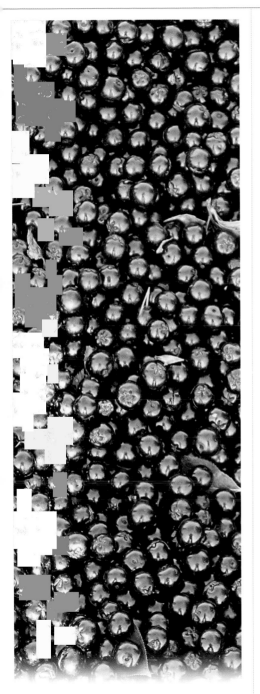

5. "Grandparents antioxidant paradox":

It looks like our grandparents were able to manufacture alcoholic beverages with excellent properties from local fruits and berries! Fruit wines prepared at home, according to the old recipes, exhibited strong antioxidant properties, comparable to that of red grape wine.

6. "Polish antioxidant paradox".

Increased consumption of Aronia fruits in Poland may lower the risk of heart disease; it creates a chance for a **"Polish antioxidant paradox"**. Aronia is a rich source of antioxidants, promising for their cardiovascular protective effects.

7. "American paradox".

Aronia melanocarpa which is native to Canada and the USA is not popular there. Increased production and consumption of Aronia berries in America is a chance for **"American antioxidant paradox"**, e.g. lower risk of heart infarct, like in south France.

FREQUENT ABBREVIATIONS AND DEFINITIONS

ROS - reactive oxygen species

RNS – reactive nitrogen species

superoxide anion: $O_2^{\bullet -}$;

hydroperoxyl radical: $HO_2^{\bullet}$

hydrogen peroxide: H_2O_2

hydroxyl radical: $OH^{\bullet}$

peroxynitrite anion: $ONOO-$

nitric oxide: $NO^{\bullet}$

oxidative stress -

excess production of ROS and RNS in the cells

EPR, electron paramagnetic resonance –

the best method of detection and studies of free radicals

NMR, nuclear magnetic resonance –

most popular ^1H and ^{13}C NMR enables identification and structural studies of organic compounds in the solution and solid phase

The free-radical hypothesis of aging:

states that accumulation of oxidative damage to biomolecules is the major underlying cause of senescence and degenerative diseases.

Phytamins :

antioxidants and radical scavengers absorbed from plant foods, mainly **bioflavonoids** (not synthesized by human body, like vitamins).

Food supplement (dietary supplement) –

means foodstaffs the purpose of which is to supplement the normal diet which are concentrated sources of nutrients or other substances with a nutritional or physiological effect, alone or in combination, marketed in dose form (capsules, pastilles, tablets, pills and other similar forms, sachets or powder, ampoules of liquids, drop dispensing bottles and other similar forms of liquids and powders) designed to be taken in small, measured quantities.

REFERENCES

[1] R.G. Saifutdinov, L.I. Larona, T.I. Vakul'skaya and M.G. Voronkov, Electron Paramagnetic Resonance in Biochemistry and Medicine, Kluwer Academic/Plenum Publishers, New York, 2001

[2] C.A. Rice-Evans and L. Packer, Eds., Flavonoids in Health and Disease, Second edition, Marcel Dekker Inc., New York, 2003

[3] Y. J. Suzuki, H. J. Forman, A. Sevanian, "Oxidants as stimulators of signal transduction", Free Radic. Biol. Med. 22 (1997) 269-285

[4] H. Schroeter, C.Boyd, J.P.E. Spencer, et al., "MAP signalling in neurodegeneration: influences of flavonoids and of nitric oxide", Neurobiol. Aging 23 (2002) 861-880

[5] S.A.B.E. van Acker, M.N.J.L. Tromp, G.R.M.M. Haenen, et al., "Flavonoids as scavengers of nitric oxide radical", Biochem. Biophys. Res. Commun. 214 (1995) 755-759

[6] T. Ichiyanagi, Y. Hatano, S. Matsuo, T. Konishi, "Simultaneous comparison of relative reactivities of twelve major anthocyanins in bilberry towards reactive nitrogen species". Chem. Pharm. Bull. (Tokyo). 52(11) (2004) 1312-5

[7] R.J. Williams, J.P.E. Spencer, C. Rice-Evans, "Flavonoids: antioxidants or signalling molecules?", Free Radic. Biol.Med., 36 (2004) 838-849

[8] K. Ishige, D. Schubert, Y. Saraga, "Flavonoids protect neuronal cells from oxidative stress by three distinct mechanisms", Free Radic. Biol. Med. 30 (2001) 433-446

[9] B.J. Willcox, K. Yano, R. Chen, et al. "How much should we eat? The association between energy intake and mortality in a 36-year follow-up study of Japanese-American men", J. Gerontol. A. Biol. Sci. Med. Sci. 59(8) (2004) 789-95

[10] A.E. Stapleton, V. Walbot, "Flavonoids can protect maize DNA from the induction of UV damage", Plant Physiology 105 (1994) 881-889

[11] J.P. Schnitzler, T.P. Jungblut, C. Feicht, M. Kofferlein, C. Langobartek, W. Heller, H. Sanderman "UV-B screening pigments and chalcone synthase mRNA in needles of Scots pine seedlings", New Physiologist 132 (1996) 247-258

[12] M.N. Merzlyak, O.B. Chivkunova, "Light-stress-induced pigment changes and evidence for antho-

cyanin photoprotection in apples", J. Photochem. Photobiol. 55 (2000) 155-163

[13] H. Kurata, A. Mochizuki, N. Okuda, et al., "Intermittent light irradiation with second- and hour-scale periods controls anthocyanin production by strawberry cells", Enz. Microb. Technol. 26 (2000) 621-629

[14] S. Krisa, P.W. Teguo, A. Decendit, et al., "Production of 13C-labelled anthocyanins by Vitis vinifera cell suspension cultures", Phytochem.51 (1999) 651-656

[15] B.Q. Li, T. Fu, Y.D. Yan, "Inhibition of HIV by baicalin", Cell. Mol. Biol. Res. 39 (1997) 119-124

[16] B. Malhotra, J.C. Onyilagha, B.A. Bohm, et al., "Inhibition of tomato ring-spot virus by flavonoids", Phytochem. 50 (1996) 1271- 1276

[17] J.A. Vinson, X. Su, L. Zubik, P. Bose, "Phenol antioxidant quantity and quality in foods: fruits", J.Agric. Food Chem. 49 (2001) 5315-5321

[18] N.P. Seeram, "Berry fruits: compositional elements, biochemical activities, and the impact of their intake on human health, performance, and disease". J. Agric. Food Chem. 56 (2008) 627-9

[19] M. Heinonen, "Antioxidant activity and antimicrobial effect of berry phenolics - a Finnish perspective". Mol. Nutr. Food Res. 51 (2007) 684-91

[20] R.L. Prior, G. Cao, A. Martin et al., "Antioxidant capacity as influenced by total phenolic and anthocyanin content, maturity and variety of Vaccinium species", J. Agric. Food Chem. 46 (1998) 2686-2693

[21] M.P. Kähkönen, A.I. Hopia, M. Heinonen, "Berry phenolics and their antioxidant activity", J. Agric. Food Chem. 49 (2001) 4076-4082

[22] I. M. Heinonen, P.J. Lehtonen and A.I. Hopia, "Antioxidant activity of berry and fruit wines and liquors", J. Agric. Food Chem. 46 (1998) 25-31

[23] J. Oszmianski., J.C. Sapis, "Anthocyanins in the fruits of Aronia melanocarpa (black chockeberry)" J. Food Sci. 53 (1988) 1241-1242

[24] J. Oszmiański, A. Kucharska, "Taniny aronii", Zeszyty Naukowe AR we Wrocławiu, Technologia Żywności VIII, 273 (1995) 55-64

[25] J. Oszmiański, J. C. Sapis, "Hydroxycinnamic acid derivatives in fruits of aronia melanocarpa Elliot", Zeszyty Naukowe AR we Wrocławiu, Technologia Żywności V, (1989) 75-87

[26] M. Balcerek, Optymalizacja technologii otrzymywania spirytusu aroniowego, PhD Thesis, Technical University of Łódź, 2001

[27] J. Wilska-Jeszka, J. Łoś, M. Pawlak, "Fruits as bioflavonoids sources", Acta Aliment. Polonica XVII (XLI) (1991) 11-19

[28] A.W. Strigl, E. Leitner., W. Pfannhauser, "Die Schwarze Apfelbeere (Aronia melanocarpa) als naturliche Farbstoffquelle", Deutsche Lebensmittel- Rundschau 91 (1995) 177-180

[29] B. Berente, D. De la Calle Garcia, M. Reichenbacher, K. Danzer, "Method development for the determination of anthocyanins in red wines by HPLC and classification of German red wines by means of multivariante statistical methods", J. Chromatogr.A 871 (2000) 95-103

[30] W. Zheng, S.Y. Wang, "Oxygen radical absorbing capacity of phenolic in blueberries, cranberries, chockeberries and lingonberries", J. Agric. Food Chem. 51 (2003) 502-509

[31] L. Gu, M. Kelm, J. F. Hammerstone et.al., "Fractionaction of polymeric procyanidins from lowbush blueberry and quantification of procyanidins in selected foods with an optimised normal-phase HPLC-MS fluoresent detection method", J. Agric. Food. Chem. 50 (2002) 4852-4860

[32] T. Fossen, S. Rayyan, O.M. Andersen, "Dimeric anthocyanins from strawberry (Fragaria ananassa) consisting of pelargonidin 3-glucoside covalently linked to four flavan-3-ols", Phytochem. 65 (2004) 1421-1428

[33] Y. Kono, S. Kashine, T. Yoneyama, Y. Sakamoto, "Iron chelation by chlorogenic acid as a natural antioxidant", Biosci. Biotech. Biochem. 62 (1998) 22-27

[34] R. Choudhury, S.K. Srai, E. Debnam, C.A. Rice-Evans, "Urinary extrection of hydroxycinnamates and flavonoids after oral and intravenous administration", Free Radic. Biol. Med. 27 (1999) 278-286

[35] M.R. Olthof, P.C. Hollman, M.N. Buijsman, J.M. van Amelsvoort, M.B. Katan, "Chlorogenic acid, quercetin-3-rutinoside and black tea phenols are extensively metabolized in humans", J. Nutr. 133(6) (2003) 1806-14

[36] D.V. Rodriguez de Sotillo, M. Hadley, "Chlorogenic acid modifies plasma and liver concentrations of: cholesterol, triacylglycerol, and minerals in (fa/fa) Zucker rats", J. Nutr. Biochem. 13 (2002) 717-72

[37] L. Panzella, A. Napolitano, M. d'Ischia, "Oxidative conjugation of chlorogenic acid with glutatione: structural characterization of addition products and a new nitrite-promoted pathway", Bioorg. Med. Chem. 11 (2003) 4797-4805

[38] K. Weinges, H. Schick, H. Irngartinger, T. Oeser, "Composition of an anthocyan concentrate from Aronia melanocarpa Elliot – x-ray analysis of tetraacetyl parasorboside", Eur. J. Org. Chem. (1998), 189-192

39 A. Razungles, J. Oszmianski, J-C. Sapis, "Determination of carotenoids in fruits of Rosa sp.(Rosa canina and Rosa rugosa) and of Chokeberry (Aronia melanocarpa)", J. Food. Sci. 54 (3), (1989) 774-775

40 K. Milton, "Nutritional character-istics of wild primate foods: do the diets of our closest living relatives have lessons for us?" Nutrition 15(6) (1999) 488-498

41 E. Lev, "Reconstructed materia medica of the Medieval and Ottoman al-Sham", J. Ethnopharma-col. 80(2-3), (2002) 167-179

42 B. Smolkova, M. Dusinska, K. Raslova, et al., "Seasonal changes in markers of oxidative damage to lipids and DNA; correlations with seasonal variation in diet", Mutat. Res. 551 (2004) 135-144

43 S. O. Keli, M. G. Hertog, E.J. Feskens, D. Kromhout, "Dietary flavonoids, antioxidant vitamins and incidence of stroke: the Zutphen study". Arch. Intern. Med. 156 (1996) 637-642

44 K. Imai, K. Nakachi, "Cross sec-tional study of effects of drinking green tea on cardiovascular and liver diseases", BMJ 310 (1995) 693-696

45 P. Knekt, R. Jarvinen, R. Seppa-nen, M. Hellovaara et al., "Dietary flavonoids and risk of cancer and other malignant neoplasms", Am. J. Epidemiol. 146 (1997) 223-230

46 K. T. Khaw, S. Bingham, A. Welch, et al., "Relation between plasma ascorbic acid and mortality in men and women in EPIC-Norfolk prospective study: a prospective pop-ulation study. European Prospective Investigation into Cancer and Nutri-tion", Lancet 357 (2001) 657-663

47 N.G. Stephens, A. Parsons, P.M. Schofield, et al., "Randomised con-trolled trial of vitamin E in patient with coronary disease: Cambridge Heart Antioxidant Study (CHAOS)", Lancet 347 (1996) 781-786

48 I.D. Podmore, H.R.Griffits, K.E. Herbert, et al., "Vitamin C exhibits pro-oxidant properties", Nature, 392 (1998) 559

49 B. Halliwell, "The antioxidant paradox", Lancet, 355 (2000) 1179-1180

50 B. Halliwell, "Free radicals, antioxidants and human disease: curiosity, cause or consequence?", Lancet 344 (1994) 721-724

51 M. Meydani, "Vitamin E", Lancet 345 (1995) 170-175; M. Meydani, "Nutrition interventions in aging and cardiovascular disease". Proceedings of the Nutrition Society 161 (2002) 165-171

52 S. T. Mayne, "Beta-carotene, carotenoids and disease prevention in humans", FASEB J. 10 (1996) 690-701

53 W. A. Pryor, W. Stahl, C.L. Rock, "Beta-carotene: from biochemistry to clinical trials", Nutr. Rev. 58 (2000) 39-53

54 G. S. Omenn, G. E. Godman, M.D. Thornquist et al., "Effects of a combination of beta-carotene and vitamin A on lung cancer and cardio-vascular disease", N. Engl. J. Med. 334 (1996) 1150-1155

55 C. F. Skibola, M.T. Smith, "Potential health impacts of exten-sive flavonoid intake", Free Radic. Biol. Med. 29 (2000) 375-383

56 S. Renaud, M. deLorgeril, "Wine, alcohol, platelets and the French paradox for coronary heart disease", Lancet 339 (1992) 1523-1526; E.N. Frankel, J. Kanner, J.B. German, E.Parks, J.E.Kinsella, "Inhibition of oxidation of human low-density lipoprotein by phenolic substances in red wine", Lancet 341 (1993) 454-457; E.N. Frankel, A.L. Waterhouse, J.E. Kinsella, "Inhibition of human low density lipoprotein oxidation by resveratrol", Lancet 341 (1993) 1103-1104

57 F. Natella, A. Ghiselli, A. Guidi, et al., "Red wine mitigates the post-prandial increase of LDL susceptibili-ty to oxidation", Free Radic. Biol. Med. 30 (2001) 1036-1044

58 L.L. Stanley, J.P. Mazier, "Poten-tial explanations for the French para-dox", Nutr. Res. 19 (1999) 3-15

59 J.A. Russel, M.S. Rohrbach, "Tannin induces endothelium-depen-dent contraction and relaxation of rabbit pulmonary artery", Am. Rev. Respirat. Dis. 139 (1989) 498-503

60 A.A. E. Bertelli, "Wine, research and cardiovascular disease: Instruc-tions for use", Atherosclerosis, 195 (2007) 242–247

61 E. Haslam, "In vino veritas: oligomeric procyanidins and the aging of red wines", Phytochem. 19 (1980) 2577-2582

62 H. Fulkrand, P.J. Cameira dos Santos, P. Sarni-Manchado, V. Cheynier, J. Favre-Bonvin, "Struc-ture of new anthocyanin-derived wine pigments", J. Chem.Soc. Perkin Trans. 1 (1996) 735-739

63 R. Brouillard, S. Chassaing, A. Fougerousse, "Why are grape/fresh wine anthocyanins so simple and why is it that red wine color lasts so long?", Phytochem. 64 (2003) 1179-1186

64 A. Dickinson, N. Boyon, A. Shao, "Physicians and nurses use and rec-ommend dietary supplements: report of a survey", Nutrition J. 8 (2009) 29

65 T.Y. Cheng, Z. Zhu, S. Masuda, N.C. Morcos, "Effects of multinutri-ent supplementation on antioxidant defense systems in healthy human beings", J. Nutr. Biol. 12 (2002) 388-395

[66] G. Block, Ch. D Jensen, E. P Norkus et al. "Usage patterns, health, and nutritional status of long-term multiple dietary supplement users: a cross-sectional study" Nutrition Journal, 6 (2007) 30, 1-11

[67] B. Thompson, W. Demark-Whanefried, G. Taylor, J.W. McClelland et al., "Baseline fruit and vegetable intake among adults in seven 5 A Day study centers located in diverse geographic areas", J. Am. Diet. Assoc. 99 (1999) 1241-1248

[68] L.V. Joergensen, H.L. Madsen, M.K. Thomsen, et al., "Regeneration of phenolic antioxidants from phenoxyl radicals: an ESR and electrochemical study of antioxidant hierarchy", Free Radic. Res. 30 (1999) 207-230

[69] C. Rice-Evans, N.J. Miller, G. Paganga, "Structure-antioxidant activity of flavonoids and phenolic acids", Free Radic. Biol. Med. 20 (1996) 933-956

[70] M.P. Kahkonen, M. Heinonen. "Antioxidant activity of anthocyanins and their aglycons", J. Agric. Food Chem. 51(3), (2003) 628-33

[71] T. Yoshida, K. Mori, T. Hatano, et al., "Studies on inhibition mechanism of autoxidation by tannins and flavonoids. V. Radical scavenging effects of tannins and related polyphenols on DPPH radical", Chem. Pharm. Bull. 37 1919-1921 (1989); T. R. Hatano, M. Edamatsu, M. Hiramatsu et al., "Effects of the interaction of tannins with co-existing substances.VI. Effects of tannins and related polyphenols on superoxide anion radical and on DPPH radical", Chem. Pharm. Bull. 37 (1989) 2016-2021

[72] N. Pellegrini, M. Serafini, B. Colombi, et al., "Total antioxidant capacity of plant foods, beverages and oils consumed in Italy assessed by three different in vitro assays", J. Nutr. 133 (2003) 2812-2819

[73] A. Horubała, "Pojemność przeciwutleniająca i jej zmiany w procesach przetwarzania owoców i warzyw", Przem. Ferm. i Owoc.Warzyw. 3 (1999) 30-32

[74] W. Zheng, S.Y. Wang, "Oxygen radical absorbing capacity of phenolics in blueberries, cranberries, chockeberries and lingonberries", J. Agric. Food Chem. 51 (2003) 501-509

[75] M.P. Kähkönen, A.I. Hopia, M. Heinonen, "Berry phenolics and their antioxidant activity", J.Agric. Food Chem., 49 (2001) 4076-4082

[76] R.A.Moyer, K.E. Hummer, C.E. Finn, et al., "Anthocyanins, phenolics and antioxidant capacity in diverse small fruits: Vaccinium, Rubus and Ribes", J.Agric.Food Chem. 50 (2002) 519-525

[77] H. Wang, G.Cao, RL Prior, "Total antioxidant capacity of fruits", J.Agric.Food Chem. 44 (1996) 701-704

[78] R.L. Prior, G. Cao, A. Martin, et al., "Antioxidant capacity as influenced by total phenolic and anthocyanin content, maturity and variety of Vaccinium species", J. Agric. Food Chem. 46 (1998) 2686-2693

[79] P. Morazzoni, S. Livio, A. Scilingo, S. Malandrino, "Vaccinium myrtillus anthocyanosides pharmacokinetics in rats", Arzneimittelforschung 41 (1991) 128-131

[80] K.A. Youdim, B. Shukitt-Hale. S. MacKinnon, W. Kalt., J.A. Joseph, "Polyphenolics enhance red blood cell resistance to oxidative stress: in vitro and in vivo", Biochim. Biophys. Acta - Gen.Subj. 1523 (2000) 117-122

[81] T. Lapidot, S.H. Granit, J. Kanner., "Bioavailability of red wine anthocyanins as detected in human urine", J. Agric. Food Chem. 46 (1998) 4297-4300

[82] M. Murkovic, H. Toplak, U. Adam, W. Pfannhauser, "Analysis of anthocyanins in plasma for determination of their bioavailability", J. Food Comp. Anal. 13 (2000) 291-296

[83] P.E. Milbury, G. Cao, R.L. Prior, J. Blumberg, "Bioavailability of elderberry anthocyanins", Mech.Ageing Develop. 123 (2002) 997-1066

[84] C.D. Kay, G. Mazza, B.J. Holub, J. Wang, "Anthocyanin metabolites in human urine and serum", Br. J. Nutr. 91(6) (2004) 933-942.

[85] I. Bitsch, M. Janssen, M. Netzel, et al., "Bioavailability of anthocyanidin-3-glycosides following consumption of elderberry extract and blackcurrant juice", Int. J. Clin. Pharmacol. Ther. 42(5), (2004) 293-300.

[86] T. Ichiyanagi, M.M. Rahman, Y. Kashiwada et al., "Absorption and metabolism of delphinidin-2-O-glucopyranoside in rats", Free Radic. Biol. Med. 36 (2004) 930-937

[87] T. Ichiyanagi, Y Shida, MM Rahman, et al., "Metabolic pathway of cyanidin 3-O-beta-D-glucopyranoside in rats", J. Agric. Food Chem. 53(1) (2005) 145-150.

[88] A.R. Proteggente, A. Saija, A. de Pasquale, C. A. Rice-Evans, Free Radic. Res. 37 (6) (2003) 681-687

[89] F. Galvano, L. La Fauci, G. Lazzarino, et al., "Cyanidins: metabolism and biological properties", J. Nutr. Biochem. 15 (2004) 2-11

[90] U. Mulleder, M. Murkovic, W. Pfannhauser, "Urinary excretion of cyanin glycosides", J. Biochem. Biophys. Methods 53 (2002) 61-66

[91] M. Netzel, G. Strass, C. Kaul et al., "In vivo antioxidative capacity of a composite berry juice", Food Res. Internat., 35 (2002) 213-216

[92] C. Ramirez-Tortosa, O.M. Andersen, P.T. Gardner, et al., "Anthocyanin-rich extract decreases indices of lipid peroxidation and DNA damage in vitamin E-depleted rats", Free

Radic. Biol. Med. 31 (2001) 1033-1037

93 M. Harada, Y. Kan, H. Naoki et al., "Identification of the major antioxidative metabolites in biological fluids of the rat with ingested catechin and epicatechin", Biosci. Biotechnol. Biochem. 63 (1999) 973-977

94 M. Natsume, N. Osakabe, M. Oyama, et al., "Structures of (-)-epicatechin glucuronide identified from plasma and urine after oral ingestion of (-)-epicatechin: differences between human and rat". Free Radic. Biol. Med. 34 (2003) 840-849

95 S. Baba, N. Osakabe, M. Natsume, J.Terao "Absorption and urinary excretion of procyanidin B2 [epicatechin-(4,-8)-epicatechin] in rats", Free Radic Biol Med. 33(1) (2002) 142-8.

96 RR. Holt, S.A. Lazarus, MC. Sullards et al., "Procyanidin dimer B2 [epicatechin-(4ß-8)-epicatechin] in human plasma after the consumption of a flavanol-rich cocoa", Am. J. Clin. Nutr. 76 (2002) 798-804

97 S.B. Lotito, L. Actis-Goretta, M.L. Renart, et al., "Influence of oligomer chain length on the antioxidant activity of procyanidins", Biochem. Biophys. Res. Commun. 276(3) (2000) 945-51.

98 N. Ryszawa, A. Kawczyńska-Dróżdż, J. Pryjma et.al. "Effects of novel plant antioxidants on platelet superoxide production and aggregation" Atheroscler. J. Physiol.Pharm. 57 (2006) 611-626

99 M. Naruszewicz, I. Łaniewska, B. Millo, M. Dłużniewski, "Combination therapy of statin with flavonoids rich extract from chokeberry fruits enhanced reduction in cardiovascularrisk markers in patients after myocardial infraction (MI)". Atherosclerosis 194 (2007) e179–e184

100 M. Heinonen, A.S. Meyer, E.N. Frankel, "Antioxidant activity of berry phenolics on human low density lipoprotein and liposome oxidation", J. Agric. Food Chem. 46 (1998) 4107-4112

101 T. Lapidot, S. Harel, B. Akiri, R. Granit, J. Kanner, pH-Dependent forms of red wine anthocyanins as antioxidants, J.Agric.Food Chem., 47 (1999) 67-70

102 A.J. Burns, I.R. Rowland, "Antigenotoxicity of probiotics and prebiotics on faecal water-induced DNA damage in human colon adenocarcinoma cells", Mutat. Res. 551 (2004) 233-243

103 A.N. Freedman, A. M. Michalek, J.R. Marshall, et.al., "Familial and nutritional risk factors for p53 over-expression in colorectal cancer", Cancer Epidemiol. Biomarkers Prev. 5 (1996) 285-291

104 L.R. Fergusson, P.J. Harris, "The dietary fiber debate: more food for thought", Lancet 361 (2003) 1487-1488

105 B. Halliwell, "Effect of diet on cancer development: is oxidative DNA damage a biomarker?", Free Radic. Biol. Med. 32 (2002) 968-974

106 R. Acquaviva, A. Russo, F. Galvano, et al., "Cyanidin and cyanidin 3-O-beta-D -glucoside as DNA cleavage protectors and antioxidants", Cell Biol. Toxicol. 19(4), (2003) 243-52.

107 K. Gąsiorowski, K. Szyba, B. Brokos, et al., "Antimutagenic activity of anthocyjanins isolated from Aronia melanocarpa fruits", Cancer Lett. 119 (1997) 37-46

108 C. Zhao, M.M. Giusti, M. Malik, et al., "Effects of commercial anthocyanin-rich extracts on colonic cancer and nontumorigenic colonic cell growth", J. Agric. Food Chem. 52(20), (2004) 6122-6128.

109 S.Y. Kang, N.P. Seeram, M.G. Nair, L.D. Bourquin, "Tart cherry anthocyanins inhibit tumor development in Apc(Min) mice and reduce proliferation of human colon cancer cells", Cancer Lett. 194(1), (2003) 13-19

110 D.X. Hou, T. Ose, S. Lin, et al., "Anthocyanidins induce apoptosis in human promyelocytic leukemia cells: structure-activity relationship and mechanisms involved", Int. J. Oncol. 23(3), (2003) 705-712

111 J. Sun, Y.-F. Chu, X. Wu, R.H. Liu, "Antioxidant and antiproliferative activities of common fruits", J. Agric. Food Chem. 50 (2002) 7449-7454

112 L. Favot, S. Martin, T. Keravis, et al., "Involvement of cyclin-dependent pathway in the inhibitory effect of delphinidin on angiogenesis", Cardiovasc. Res. 59, (2003) 479-487.

113 D.X. Hou, M. Fujii, N. Terahara, M. Yoshimoto, "Molecular mechanisms behind the chemopreventive effects of anthocyanidins", J. Biomed. Biotechnol. 2004 (5), (2004) 321-325

114 S. Roy, S. Khanna, H.M. Alessio, et.al.. "Anti-angiogenic property of edible berries", Free Radic. Res. 36 (2002) 1023-31.

115 M.F. Beal, "Oxidatively modified proteins in aging and disease", Free Radic. Biol. Med. 32 (2002) 797-803

116 K.A. Youdim, J.A. Joseph, "A possible role of phytochemicals in improving age-related neurological dysfunctions: a multiplicity of effects", Free Radic. Biol. Med. 30 (2001) 583-594

117 N. Nishiyama, T. Moriguchi, H. Saito, "Beneficial effects of aged garlic extract on lerning and memory impairment in the senescence-accelerated mouse", Exp. Gerontol. 32 (1997) 149-160

118 J.A. Joseph, B. Shukitt-Hale, N.A. Denisova, et al., "Long-term dietary strawberry, spinach or vitamin E supplementation retards the onset of age-related neuronal signal-

transduction and cognitive behavioral deficits", J. Neurosci. 18 (1998) 8047-8055; J.A. Joseph, B. Shukitt-Hale, N.A. Denisova, et al., "Reversals of age-related declines in neuronal signal transduction, cognitive and motor behavioral deficits with diets supplemented with blueberry, spinach or strawberry dietary supplementation", J. Neurosci. 19 (1999) 8114-8121

119 K.A. Youdim, B. Shukitt-Hale, A. Martin et al., "Short term dietary supplementation of blueberry polyphenolics: beneficial effects on aging brain performance and peripherial tissue function", Nutr. Neurosci. 3 (2000) 383-397

120 J.A. Joseph, N.A. Denisova, G. Arendash, et al., "Blueberry supplementation enhances signalling and prevents behavioral deficits in an Alzheimer disease model", Nat. Neurosci. 6 (2003) 153-162

121 K.A. Youdim, M.S. Dobbie, G. Kuhnle, et al., "Interaction between flavonoids and the blood-brain barrier: in vitro studies", J. Neurochem. 85 (2003) 180-192.

122 H. Toghi, T. Abe, K. Yamazaki, et al., "Alternations of 3-nitrotyrosine concentration in the cerebrospinal fluid during aging and in patients with Alzheimers disease", Neurosci. Letters 269 (1999) 52-54

123 Y-T.Choi, C-H.Jung, S-R.Lee, et al., "The green tea polyphenol (-)-epigallocatechin gallate attenuates β-amyloid-induced neurotoxicity in cultured hippocampal neurons", Life Sci. 70 (2001) 603-614

124 T. Tsuda, Y. Kato, T.Osawa, "Mechanism for the peroxynitrite scavenging activity by anthocyanins", FEBS Lett. 484 (2000) 207-210

125 P.F. Good, A. Hsu, P. Werner, et al., "Protein nitration in Parkinson disease", J. Neuropathol. Exp. Neurol., 57 (1998) 338-339

126 A.Y. Sun, A. Simonyl, G.Y. Sun, "The 'French paradox' and beyond: neuroprotective effects of polyphenols", Free Radic. Biol. Med. 32 (2002) 314-318

127 C. Delcourt, J.P. Cristol, F. Tessier, et al., "Age-related macular degradation and antioxidant status in the POLA study. POLA study group. Pathologies Occulaires Liees a l'Age", Arch. Ophtalmol. 117 (1999) 1384-1390

128 T. Lapidot, S. Harel, B. Akiri, R. Granit, J. Kanner, pH-Dependent forms of red wine anthocyanins as antioxidants, J.Agric.Food Chem., 47 (1999) 67-70

129 J.A. Simon, E.S. Hudes, "Serum ascorbic acid and other correlates of self reported cataract among older Americans", J. Clin. Epidemiol. 52 (1999) 1207-1211

[130] M.P. Valero, A.E. Fletcher, B.L. De Stavola, J. Vioque, V.C. Alepuz, "Vitamin C is associated with reduced risk of cataract in a Mediterranean population", J. Nutr. 132(6), (2002) 1299-1306

[131] J. Lutomski, "'Klarin' – na lepsze widzenie", Postępy fitoterapii 6 (2001) 25-27

[132] P. Morazzoni, E. Bombardelli, "Vaccinium myrtillus", Fitoterapia, 1996, LXVII, 3-29; M.T. Murray, "Bilberry (Vaccinium myrtillus)", Am. J. Nat. Med. 4 (1997) 18-22

[133] P.H. Canter, E. Ernst. "Anthocyanosides of Vaccinium myrtillus (bilberry) for night vision--a systematic review of placebo-controlled trials", Surv. Ophthalmol. 49, (2004) 38-50

[134] E.R. Muth, J.M. Laurent, P. Jasper, "The effect of bilberry nutritional supplementation on night visual acuity and contrast sensitivity", Altern. Med. Rev. 5 (2000) 164-173

[135] A.E. Millen, M. Gruber, R. Klein, et al., "Relations of serum ascorbic acid and alpha-tocopherol to diabetic retinopathy in the Third National Health and Nutrition Examination Survey", Am. J. Epidemiol. 158 (2003) 225-233.

[136] H. Wagner, Annual Proceedings of Phytochemical Society of Europe, 25 (1985) 409

[137] M. Miranda, M. Muriach, S. Johnsen, et al., "Oxidative stress in a model for experimental diabetic retinopathy: treatment with antioxidants", Arch. Soc. Esp. Oftalmol. 79(6) (2004) 289-94

[138] P. Pawłowicz, J. Wilczyński, G. Stachowiak, P. Hincz, "Administration of natural anthocyanins derived from chockeberry retardation of idopathic and preeclamptic origin. Influence on metabolism of plasma oxidized lipoproteins: the role of autoantibodies to oxidize low density lipoproteins", Ginecol. Pol. 71 (2000) 848-853

[139] A. Jankowski, B. Jankowska, J. Niedworok, "The effect of anthocyanin dye from grapes on experimental diabetes", Folia Med. Cracov. 41(3-4), (2000) 5-15

[140] B. Jayaprakasam, S.K. Vareed, L.K. Olson, M.G. Nair, "Insulin secretion by bioactive anthocyanins and anthocyanidins present in fruits", J. Agric. Food Chem. 53 (2005) 28-31.

[141] C.Y. Lu, H-C Lee, H-J.Fahn, Y-H. Wei, "Oxidative damage elicited by imbalance of free radical scavenging enzymes is associated with large-scale mt-DNA deletions in aging human skin", Mutat. Res. 423 (1999) 11-21

[142] F. Bonina, M. Lanza, L. Montenegro, et al., "Flavonoids as potential protective agents against photooxidative skin damage", Int. J. Pharm. 145 (1996) 87-94

[143] E.A. Offord, J.C. Gautier, O. Avanti, et al. "Photoprotective poten-

tial of lycopene, ,-carotene, vitamin E, vitamin C and carnosic acid in UVA-irradiated human skin fibroblasts", Free Radic. Biol. Med. 32 (2002) 1293-1303

[144] C. Saliou, G. Rimbach, H. Moini, et al., "Solar ultraviolet-induced erythrema in human skin and nuclear factor kappa-B-dependent gene expression in keratinocytes are modulated by French maritime pine bark extract", Free Radic. Biol. Med. 30 (2001) 154-160

[145] J. Lee, S. Jiang N. Levine, R.R. Watson, "Carotenoid supplementation reduces erythema in human skin after simulated solar radiation exposure", Proc. Soc. Exp. Biol. Med. 219 (2000) 170-174

[146] I. R. Record, I.E. Dreosti, "Protection by black tea and green tea against UVB and UVA+B induced skin cancer in hairless mice", Mutat. Res. 422 (1998) 191-199

[147] N.P. Seeram, R.A. Momin, M.G. Nair, L.D. Bourquin, "Cyclogenase inhibitory and antioxidant cyanidin glycosides in cherries and berrie", Phytomedicine, 8(5) (2001) 362-369

[148] A. Jankowski, B. Jankowska, J. Niedworok, "The influence of Aronia melanocarpa in experimental pancreatitis", Polish Merkuriusz Lek. 8 (48) (2000) 395-398

[149] K. Charyk, Ochronny wpływ barwników antocyjaninowych w zatruciu 2-chloro-3-chloropropylo sulfidem, PhD Thesis, WAM Łódź, 1995

[150] G. Andryskowski, J. Niedworok, Z. Maziarz, B. Małkowski, Protective effect of natural anthocyanin dye on experimental radiation sickness, Acta Pol. Toxycol. 6 (1998) 155-162; G. Andryskowski, J. Niedworok, Z. Maziarz, B. Małkowski, The effect of anthocyanin dye on superoxide radical generation and chemiluminescence in animal after absorbed 4Gy dose of gamma-radiation, Pol.J. Environm. 7 (1998) 537-541

[151] M. Wolniak, G. Andryskowski, I. Wawer, unpublished results

[152] S. Uchida, M. Ozaki, K. Suzuki, et al., "Radioprotective effects of (-)epigallocatechin 3-O-gallate (green tea tannin) in mice", Life Sci. 50 (1992), 147-152

[153] H. Inado, M. Onoda, "Radioprotective action of curcumin extracted from Curcuma longa L.: inhibitory effect on formation of urinary 8-hydroxy-2'deoxyguanosine, tumorigenesis, but not mortality, induced by γ-irradiation", Int. J. Rad. Oncol. Biol. Phys. 53 (2002) 735-743

[154] A. Romanenko, K. Morimura, H. Wanibuchi, et al. "Increased oxidative stress with gene alteration in urinary bladder urothelium after the Chernobyl accident", Int. J. Cancer 86 (2000) 790-798

[155] C. Sauvaget, F. Kasagi, C.A. Waldren, "Dietary factors and cancer mortality among atomic bomb survivors", Mutat. Res. 551 (2004) 145-152